TILTING AT WINDMILLS

HENRY MURPHY

TILTING AT WINDMILLS

A Spanish Year Chasing a Novel Dream

HENRY MURPHY

ORPEN PRESS

Published by
Orpen Press
Upper Floor, Unit K9
Greenogue Business Park
Rathcoole
Co. Dublin
Ireland

email: info@orpenpress.com
www.orpenpress.com

Paperback ISBN 978-1-78605-090-8
ePub ISBN 978-1-78605-091-5

Printed in Dublin by SPRINTprint Ltd

For Paula and Frank

Acknowledgements

I wish to thank:

Orpen Press for bringing *Tilting at Windmills* to fruition.

Eileen O'Brien for her excellent and encouraging editing.

Peter O'Connell for his pivotal role in what I might loosely call the development of the book. From the outset he said he wanted a novel. From the outset, what he got was 'A Year in Spain', followed quickly by 'A Year in Spain Writing a Novel'. Not what Peter wanted. Plot, narrative, a storyline was what Peter wanted. He wasn't looking for *War and Peace* he kept saying. I thought that was a bit harsh on Leo. Eventually, we got somewhere. I'm not sure it was where Peter wanted to get to but all great endeavours involve compromise. One thing is certain: good or bad, the end product is unrecognisably better than what it was before Peter got his hands on it.

Another thing Peter kept saying was to get people to read it and read it critically. So I sent it to everyone I could think of. The result is that more people have read it than haven't. I am grateful to each and every one.

I assembled a formidable team of readers in my village. Maggie Gardner, Eamonn Vincent and Luckett Bell (Eamonn and Luckett themselves scribblers of distinction) read and edited the book more than once and improved it enormously. My thanks.

At home, family excluded, I assembled an equally formidable team. I wish to acknowledge the great work of Annette Foley, Mona O'Rourke, Marian Shanley and Berna Canning. Their observations were inspiring. Very sadly, Berna died last April and so doesn't get to see the fruits of her work. And now, her husband, my life-long friend Fergus, has died also. May they read in peace.

Finally, I wish to thank Mary for her unconditional support.

Contents

1

NEW YEAR'S EVE, Praia De Rocha, Algarve

"If I understand you correctly Mark, you are retiring from the Bar", Danny summarised. He was a summarising sort of person.

"Not retiring. A year out. The kids do it. Why not me?"

"Well that's something anyway. You're not chucking the whole thing in."

"Not yet", I said and laughed.

Danny paused, puffed and resumed.

"What on earth will you do?" he asked. Not Dublin's leading entrepreneur for nothing. "Sail around the world, I suppose? Everyone's at it. Can't see what they see in it myself."

I love sailing.

"Nothing like that. I'll be working hard." Pause. "Writing."

A look of astonishment, the size of an Atlantic wave, crossed Danny's face.

"Writing?" he asked, as if he had just been told that I was divorcing Helen and entering a monastery. "Writing what?"

"A book – of course."

"A memoir? Everyone's writing memoirs."

"No."

"What then? A book on law? The Law of Easements perhaps, or Cyberspace. Something riveting."

"Nothing to do with the Law. A Novel."

Another wave crossed the Atlantic and broke across his brow. Danny had heard it all now. A fellow going on 64 taking a year out to write a novel. He went silent. So did the crickets. And the fireworks in the distance.

Human nature abhors a silence. Kate, Danny's wife, was in like a shot.

"Is he serious?" she asked her sister, my wife.

"I'm afraid he is", Helen replied. "He's been talking about this for a while. Indeed he tried it before. It's a long time ago now. He was about six years at the Bar. Things weren't going well. He was talking about journalism and giving the writing a go."

"What did you do?"

"I put my foot down of course. Said it was ridiculous. I was three months pregnant at the time."

"And now?"

"At least the circumstances are different. But I'm not so sure that you can interrupt your practice like this and hope to return. He's nearly 65 ...".

"64", I interjected.

"Solicitors move on", Helen added. "They have to. Find younger barristers."

Danny was back. It had only been a matter of time.

"Have I got this right? You're going to interrupt your practice at the Bar to write a novel?" Summarising again.

"Just for a year. One year for the novel. Then back to the Law Library. Look at Jeffrey Archer."

"What has Jeffrey Archer got to do with it? He's in jail."

"He's out. Nothing I suppose except he's written lots of novels and made pots of money."

"What's the point?"

"What's the point of anything? Some people play golf."

Danny is a keen golfer.

"What will *you* do?" Kate asked Helen.

"Continue working. Someone has to pay the bills."

"And just where will you write your novel?" Danny asked.

"The West. Up and down the Wild Atlantic Way." The most colourful firework of the evening hit the sky.

"What?" said Helen, clearly hearing this part of the plan for the first time.

"You can't be serious", said Danny.

"You're joking", said Helen.

"Now look here sunshine: a novel is one thing, the West another. Helen would go out of her mind and you'd be an alcoholic in no time. All that rain."

"Do you think?"

"I know."

"Where would you suggest?"

"If you're serious ...".

"I am."

"Spain", he replied. Without hesitation. As if he had considered it himself. "South of Spain, *Andalucía*." Another puff on the cigar. "One of those *pueblo blanco* places. That's what you want. A village by the sea, or in the mountains. Peace and quiet and sun and you can write away to your heart's content." Danny was taking me by surprise. He was becoming poetic. I had known him a long time and had never seen this side of him before. Maybe I had got him wrong. Maybe I had touched something. For the moment it was the burning end of his cigar – and it was setting fire to my thumb.

"I thought we'd be staying at home", said Helen while I sucked it.

"You can't write a novel in a cul-de-sac", I said.

"A break would do you good Helen. You're very stressed", threw in Kate.

"I am not stressed and I am not going to the West", my wife said deliberately. "I hate the West."

"Do you think we'll find one of these *pueblos blancos*?" I asked Danny as soon as the fire had been put out.

"Of course. There must be fucking hundreds of them."

Danny is an entrepreneur, not a poet.

I had asked him a simple question and he had answered it.

On that confident note, we wished one another a Happy New Year and went to bed.

* * *

New Year's Eve in the south of Portugal. A blue moon in a blue sky. Sea spreading in a fan from the garden of their splendid villa. Helen and I were spending a week there with Danny and Kate. In the distance, fireworks going off. In between, crickets enchanting. A restless soul Danny; for once he seemed relaxed puffing his annual cigar, my Christmas present to him.

I had a reputation for keeping my cards close to my chest but, on this occasion, seduced by the scent of *dama de noche* and bouquet of wine, not to mention Danny's cigar, I had said more than I had intended to.

The year 1984 had been a milestone for me ever since I had read the book of that title in the sixties. I was in my late teens at the time and, while students of English were grappling with its inner meaning, I was wondering where I might be when that far-away year came around. In those days when you were trying to decide what to do with your life, elders, in the absence of career guidance, asked helpful questions:

Where do you see yourself at 40?

Where indeed?

Where did I see myself in 1984 even?

I was studying law at the time. My father was a barrister. And his father before him. My mother a solicitor. Law was, as they say, in the family.

Questions that came and went. Like the tide. Like the year 1984 itself. By then I was thirty-four years of age. Barrister. Married. Children. Questions answered.

So another milestone took its place. *The Millennium.*

It too came. The world didn't end. Planes didn't fall to the floor. The only thing that hit the sky was the price of babysitters for the night.

Still a barrister. Now fifty years of age. Still married. Still had the children. An older and wider barrister.

When I went to the doctor for my insurance medical, he asked me if I drank too much or too little. There was only one answer to that question. And he rattled into his dictaphone, "*out of his own mouth, he drinks too much.*"

Time was running out. I was running out. Running out of milestones.

Still there was one left – my first. I was at a dance in Dublin in the sixties when I heard The Beatles' song 'When I'm Sixty-Four' for the first time. In those days we went to hops, which were held in rugby clubs. The dancing was divided into sets. Three records to a set. You got up the courage to invite a girl to dance and, at the end of the set, if you fancied her, you drew a deep breath and asked her if she would like to go again. If things continued to go well, it might be a coke and, if all your Christmases came together, you might risk towards the end of the night, "would you like to see the pitch?"

When I get older losing my hair
Many years from now ...

Sixty-four. So it became the next milestone. In the faraway. When I would be an old man.

Now all of a sudden, it was looming. I didn't feel like an old man but ...

I was getting older
I was losing my hair

A millstone, and I began to think.

At university, I had no interest in Law. I wanted to write. It was all about the English Lit Society and Dramsoc. I won a short story competition. Ten pounds and publication. I can still remember the thrill. On the strength of it, my father sent a couple of my stories to a friend of his, a well-known writer from Cork. Who didn't think much of them.

"Don't encourage him", he had said to my father at the time. My father was an encouraging type of person and didn't tell me this until a long time after. But he did say that one story in the university rag and rejection by a well-known writer from Cork wasn't a platform on which to launch a literary career.

So, I stuck with Law. Consigned my writing portfolio to the bottom drawer and some unspecified date in the future.

Now, with the last of the fireworks still echoing in the distance, I sensed my final chance. Fulfilment beckoned, if belatedly.

NEW YEAR'S RESOLUTION: ONE YEAR, ONE NOVEL.

2

JANUARY

"I've been thinking", Danny said the following morning.

"So have I", said Kate.

Kate was back from the *panadería*. Danny was making the coffee.

"It's a great idea", they said together.

On that note of endorsement, we, the four of us, went online to see what was available in *Andalucía* by way of *pueblo blanco*. With the virtual help of an English woman from Birmingham who was living there, a few possibilities emerged in the mountains behind Malaga.

"It has to be near Malaga." Helen had been thinking too. "I have three granddaughters at home and I'm not leaving them." This was no pious aspiration. I knew the tone. Not the West and near Malaga – Malaga airport – or not at all.

7

By the end of our New Year stay in Portugal, progress had been made in Spain. A number of mountains close to Malaga had been identified and even a number of *pueblos blancos* and an appointment made with the helpful English woman from Birmingham. Helen had to get back home and, as my gap year was just beginning, it was agreed that I would do the field work.

Destination, Malaga. A fellow in his sixties on a mission. A double mission. A *pueblo blanco* to call his own and a novel.

Me and *Andalucía*. In her flamenco-red dress. I was excited. It could have been the Sahara, such was my sense of adventure.

No hurry. I went by bus to Seville. According to my book, the capital of *Andalucía*. It would be late when I arrived. I texted Helen. Maybe she could find me a hotel for the night on the internet. There had to be some advantage to being an explorer in the twenty-first century. Just because Lawrence couldn't text ahead and book a tent for the night was no reason why I should risk not having a place to lay my head. For all I knew, the bulls might be running the streets and there mightn't be a bed to be had.

Helen came up trumps.

"Mr Barrington, I presume?" The charming receptionist could hardly go wrong. With my jacket over my shorts, I was as unlikely as Dr Livingstone to be anyone else. The hotel was old-fashioned and lovely with a Christmas tree in the foyer. Not a bull in sight. The receptionist said I was lucky to get a room as it was Three Kings. Some rock band on tour I assumed.

The following morning was hot for January. No sign of winter in Seville. According to the writer H.V. Morton, there is much to see in Seville but, as I didn't intend to live there in the immediate future, it would have to wait. For the moment as I dragged my bag across the city, a glimpse of the *Giralda* was all I could manage.

Helen thought I was going straight to Malaga, straight to the mountains and the villages awaiting my inspection. So did I. Until the night before when I got to thinking. Paroled briefly, it seemed ungrateful not to take advantage of the opportunity which presented. Was this not the land of *Don Quixote* and windmills? Ok so you want to be pedantic, *La Mancha* is further north. Why straight to Malaga? All in good time.

Malaga later in the week. Over dinner, I plotted a new course promising a more rounded flavour of what *Andalucía* has to offer. *Pueblos blancos* are not confined to the mountains behind Malaga after all. And were there not other airports in the south of Spain from which Helen could fly home to see her grandchildren as often as she chose? It seemed a strange way to embark on a year out, wondering how best you could get back.

I decided to continue travelling by bus. A mode of transport more in keeping with my new calling as a writer, I thought. Even bought a notebook in which to jot down observations and noteworthy incidents. The notebook and Morton's *A Stranger in Spain* were my sole companions until a stranger from Patagonia tried to pick me up on the terrace of the parador in *Arcos de la Frontera* as the sun went down. My second day. My first entry.

I was enjoying a gin – Bombay sapphire – and tonic, and reading my book when he asked if he could join me. I didn't wish to be disturbed. In particular, I didn't want to have to speak. It was that magical time of the day. Warm. Wondrous colours dancing in the sky. The sun would not be around for much longer. I had the terrace, overlooking the rest of the south of Spain, to myself. At least until that moment. What prompts a member of the human race to intrude like that?

"Of course", I said. What else could I say?

"*A Stranger in Spain*", he said aloud as he picked up my book. A bit familiar I thought, even if he was well-dressed.

"Are you enjoying it?" he asked, sitting down.

"Enormously", I replied. "Second time in fact. Have you read it yourself?"

"I certainly have. In Spanish." He looked Spanish. "I'm from Patagonia."

"Ah." That explained why he read it in Spanish. It didn't explain how he spoke perfect English without an accent.

"I've read all his books. Even the ones about countries I haven't been to. I love travelling and I love reading. He's a wonderful writer."

I had no difficulty agreeing with my intruder.

"Are you a writer yourself?" he asked.

"Why do you ask?"

"Oh, I don't know. You have a look about you. I saw you from my bedroom window and you were making notes."

"You're very observant."

"I have to be. I'm a poet. Quite a good one in fact. They love me in Guatemala." This was a surprise. Not that they loved him in Guatemala but that here I was in the south of Spain in my first few days as a writer – that might be pushing it a bit – and I have this chance encounter with a poet from Patagonia. Who is loved in Guatemala.

"Have you anything published?" he continued.

"Not recently", I confessed. I didn't think my short story of forty years ago counted and I certainly wasn't going to mention the well-known writer from Cork. "I'm a lawyer from Ireland and I've decided to take a year out to write a novel." I thought I might as well let him have it.

"Good for you", he said. "A break from all that mumbo-jumbo. As it happens, my mother is a lawyer in London. I don't know how she sticks it. Dry as a cowpat in India."

"Your mother?"

"No, no. The law. Would you like a drink?"

"No thank you. I'm enjoying this." While my immediate displeasure had abated, I wasn't anxious to get too involved. He ordered a white wine for himself.

"What do you think you'll write about?"

"I don't know. I haven't decided. To be truthful I haven't a clue. Maybe something about a human rights lawyer in Ireland."

"No, no, no. Steer clear of anything to do with law. You're on a year off after all. Forgive me. Do you mind me giving you advice?" He may have been highly thought of in Guatemala but he was only half my age.

"Delighted."

"Don't write about what you know. Golden rule. Mark my words."

"Yes, but ...".

"I know. You've been told the opposite. Recipe for disaster. Good writing is all about the imagination and your imagination can't take you if you are tied to what you know."

"Now, there's food for thought."

"On that note, join me for dinner."

I was enjoying the chat but I wasn't sure where all of this was going. I explained that I was meeting my wife downtown for dinner and headed off to look for her and, hopefully, find a restaurant where he was not going to turn up.

Over my solitary dinner I made a meticulous record in my notebook of my first encounter. Who knew where in my writing adventure this might come in useful?

As luck would have it, the next morning, the poet from Patagonia and I turned up at reception at the same time to pay our bills. After our pleasant conversation on the terrace, he was keen to meet my wife. I explained that at the last moment she had changed her mind and decided to go straight to Malaga to do some shopping and we would meet there at the weekend. It wasn't great but it was the best I could do on the spur of the moment. He didn't seem to be dissatisfied with my explanation and we went our separate ways in good spirits.

"Remember what I said last night", he shouted after me. "What you don't know about."

For several days I travelled by bus. The local bus. Meandered. Time my own. No hurry. As the Spanish say, though I didn't know it then, *no prisa*. I made a plan and let it go. I stayed in a village in the mountains. I stayed in a village on the coast. *Costa de la Luz*. What a lovely name. It may not have been Ayers Rock. It may not have been Patagonia. But it was mine. My freedom. My adventure. What man of my age has the opportunity to put a rucksack on his back and go where his imagination takes him? I was beginning to see what the poet meant.

I spent my penultimate night of field work in *Jerez*, the home of sherry and amber light. The following morning, I walked past the bus station to the car rental office three streets further west. I was now under pressure to reach my appointed villages in time. Whatever about explaining to Helen that I hadn't spent the entire week in her mountains, I didn't want to have to explain that I didn't make them at all.

Desafortunadamente, my favourite Spanish word, (unfortunately, any time I try to say it, the person to whom I am speaking has moved on before I get it out), I didn't take the journey from *Jerez* to Helen's villages seriously enough. By the time I took the wrong turn into the mountains off the A7 I was already well behind time. It was getting dark and soon the signposting was of no use to me. Occasionally it told me how many kilometres to Granada. But I wasn't going to Granada. The rest of the time it gave me the names, pretty names, of mountain villages that meant nothing to anyone except the people living in them. I had made a simple mistake. I had turned off the motorway too soon and was lost. In daylight, I had some chance. In darkness, there was no way back.

I was aiming for *Sayalonga*, which hosted some of the houses I was to see – and the only hotel for miles. The signposts never mentioned it. Instead, the road climbed higher into darkness until the darkness itself disappeared. Replaced by a mountain of mist. Narrow mountain roads zigging and zagging, dicing with deathly edge. For all I knew I was driving further and further from my destination. I was tired, in severe need of severe rest and severe refreshment. Where was Helen when I needed her? She thought I was already there. Marathon runners hit a wall. I was hitting mine.

As the bells tolled the twenty-second hour of the day, I stumbled upon my destination. I parked my car in the first available space. It could have been the entrance to the fire station for all I cared. I needed a room, a stiff – very stiff – gin and tonic and something to eat. I self-diagnosed an acute case of hypoglycaemia.

I went into the first bar I could find. Where in this *pueblo blanco y oscuro* was the only hotel for miles? My enquiry gave rise to a team effort. One gentleman procured paper, another pen and a map was drawn. "B" marked the bar, "H", the hotel, simple, and a dotted line joined the two. Couldn't have been clearer. A matchstick figure dragging a bag thrown in for good measure and we all laughed. The instructions complete, they insisted I down a shot at their invitation. *Abajo, abajo* they shouted repeatedly – I didn't know what *abajo* was but I got the gist – until the last drop of the shot had disappeared. They then escorted me to the door shouting *arriba, arriba*. I didn't know what *arriba* was either but I took it to be the name of the hotel. They were pointing upwards. Brandishing my map and pulling my case, I headed in that direction, *arriba, arriba* ringing in my ears.

The morale boost I had just been given faded in step with my progress towards the hotel. It wasn't what you would call full of life. It wasn't full of anything. It was closed. How did they not know that the *Hotel Arriba*, the only hotel for miles, was closed?

Not being able to speak a word of a language is not an advantage if you are in the country where that language is spoken. It doesn't matter if you're not. I called into the shop opposite, which was barely open, and gave the elderly proprietor a piece of my mind. With particular reference to all the time I had spent learning French at school. He couldn't have been kinder, even seemed to understand that that wasn't the real issue. He sat me down and poured me a glass of sweet wine – it could have been a pint of Guinness. *Abajo, abajo*. We were off again. He pointed to my case and then to the hotel. I nodded furiously and said *si* repeatedly. Repetition seemed to be important.

He made a phone call.

A woman appeared.

She made a phone call.

No one else appeared.

She took me across the street, unlocked the door of the hotel and led me in darkness to an upstairs bedroom. It was a large hotel and, as far as I could see, empty. She gave me a key. Things were looking up.

The following morning the hotel was working like you'd expect a hotel to work. I was puzzled. I had my breakfast on the terrace overlooking a slice of the Mediterranean, 25 or so kilometres away. There was no sign of the darkness of the night before, nor the locked-upness, nor the hypoglycaemia. It was as if the previous night, in so far as the hotel was concerned, was a figment of my imagination.

"*Conas atá tú? Tá me go maith, go raibh maith agat.*"

What on earth?

I was in a godforsaken place in the backend of *Andalucía*, not in the Irish-speaking oasis of the Aran Islands. I looked around. A man of my age – he could have been my cousin from Connemara – was holding out his hand in welcome to his hotel.

"An Irish *cailín* in the past", he told me proudly. The *cúpla focal*. "I became a grandfather last night", he added almost as proudly. The closed hotel.

The helpful woman from Birmingham collected me and we looked at two houses in the village. She had been an estate agent in Malaga for five years before retiring but did not need to call on her expertise to identify their unsuitability. The first had no roof. Second, no floor. What on earth had Helen said to her? Discouraged, we drove to the next village, *Canillas de Albaida*. The only place that I hadn't driven through the night before. I walked the house. Checked for roof and floor. And a suitable room for writing. Climbed steeply to the roof terrace with its view down to the Mediterranean and up to *Maroma*, at 6,000 feet the highest mountain in the area. Irresistible. *This* was the house and *this* the village. The landlord, an English husband and wife team, seemed pleasant enough – though that wasn't really a factor as they weren't going to be living with us.

"Helen has given me plenipotentiary powers. This will do nicely." We shook hands, grabbed a coffee in Sergio's and I left for the airport. Not a minute too soon. On the plane, I looked at my diary to work out what the earliest date of return might be.

* * *

"Missed you", I said that evening in front of a roaring fire as I landed a kiss on Helen's cheek and a gin and tonic on her lap.

"Liar", she said. "I never saw such a happy smile as you waved me off."

"Nonsense. Up to a point maybe. But a whole week. When was the last time we were apart for a week?"

"Five nights."

"Very well. Five nights. Happy New Year darling."

"Happy New Year to you. How did it go? Did you get to meet our friend from Birmingham at all?"

"Yes and I have found it. It is perfect, Helen. Just what Danny ordered. A beautiful *pueblo blanco* nestling in the mountains. Peace and quiet. Far from the madding crowd, you might say. Danny was right. Hundreds of them. I must have driven through them all." Better not mention darkness and mist and getting lost. "If a fellow couldn't write a book there ...".

"And the house?"

"Lovely. Perfect in every way. You'll love it. In good nick and a room to write in."

"Air conditioning?"

Oh dear. A detail.

I forgot to ask. "Of course. You couldn't survive there without air conditioning."

"How far from the airport?" This was like being in court.

"56 kilometres. Measured it myself. Motorway." Apart from the mountain bit.

Time to turn the tables. "What about you? How did you get on with the boss?" While I was doing the spadework in *Andalucía*, all Helen had to do was ask for the year off.

"Yes and no. She has no problem in principle but she can't let me go before the summer."

"That's fine. I go now. You follow in July."

"What do you mean follow in July? We're in this together, aren't we?"

"Of course we're in it together. It's just that I'd like to start as soon as possible and you can't start till July." Obvious really.

"Do you think for a moment you'll last out there on your own for six months?"

"What do you mean?"

"Sex for one thing."

"Five months. Not going until February."

"Same difference."

"Of course I will. It's only Spain. Down the road. You might come out for my birthday."

"I'm not jumping on a plane every time you want to see me."

"Maybe it would be a good idea for me to be on my own for a while. From the writing point of view. Time to think. No distraction."

"If distraction hadn't existed, you'd have invented it."

"Maybe you don't think I'm serious about this? Maybe you don't think I'm up to it?"

"You're up to it alright. And I know you're serious. You've been going on about it long enough. But talking about it is one thing." She had a point. She always had a point.

One of my colleagues called his study the torture chamber. Refused to go in. Eventually gave up the Bar to become a carpenter. Cut the grass, play with the children, Lough Derg, anything but go into that study and close the door. Another colleague has a study and no door. Maybe that's how Helen saw this year. Another door, another study. More nagging.

"This is different", I said.

She looked up.

"What is?" she asked.

I had drifted into a court scene where we were making our respective points and this was the conclusion I had offered.

"Nothing. Just thinking. What do you say? February for me, July for you?"

"I'd prefer us to start together. It's not good to be apart like that. However, if it's not possible then so be it. February for you, July for me. And we'll see about the birthday. There had better be air conditioning."

There better be.

Another G and T.

*   *   *

I have a confession to make.

I love Spain.

My mother took me there in the sixties. I was twelve. In later years, she told my children it was because I only came second in the school sports day. We were going to Sitges, near Barcelona, for two weeks. Before it became the gay capital of the world. Until she met friends at the airport who were going to Mallorca. Whereupon we were going to Mallorca too. For the first week. Then Sitges. Those were the days. All I remember of the holiday was a ride on a camel with a fat lady and the fact that the priest wore sunglasses while saying Mass. And, that I loved every minute of it.

Over the years, holidays had brought us to many countries but our repeat business was with Spain. We started in the South, swimming pools, sun and *sangria*. Moving northwards, we discovered that there was more to Spain than *flamenco* and *paella*, though these would have been enough.

From holiday to holiday, we explored. Not in an adventurous manner. Not walking. Not on horseback. No. A hired car and a road map was the extent of our daring. We liked what we saw.

END OF MONTH REPORT

Word Count: Zero
New Spanish Phrase Learnt By Heart: *Buena Suerte* [Good Luck – Mark will need it]
Properties Acquired: One

3

FEBRUARY

Four weeks later, our plane dropped from a cloudless sky. *Aeropuerto de Costa del Sol.* Formerly *Aeropuerto de Pablo Picasso.* Obviously a wise man in *Turismo* had decided that the *Costa del Sol* brand was more profitable than *Pablo.* Georgie Best in Belfast and John Lennon in Liverpool, why not *Pablo* in Malaga? My decision had taken forty years, implementation four weeks. Made easier by the fact that I had already put professional matters in train and that, after our first week together, Helen would not be joining me in earnest until the summer. We had landed in Malaga many times but had never visited the city itself, second city of the south of Spain. This was our chance. A soft landing. A gentle introduction to what lay ahead.

A taxi left us at *Calle Larios.* Landmark street. Elegant, marble paving, long with tall buildings. Cafes alongside from which to watch the *paseo*, the ritualistic Spanish stroll. Off it, shaded tributary streets, packed with restaurants. *Teatro Romano. Alcazaba. Museo Picasso Malaga.* Newcomer *Malaga Pompidou.* A wonderful old quarter. I fell in love immediately.

We were heading to our hotel around midnight; this was February, a street party was starting up – *Carnaval de Teatro* – groups of musicians playing the streets, music and dancers filling every corner. We were tired from the journey. There would be other opportunities surely.

* * *

The following morning our bus drove east for an hour, then we turned left into the mountains, leaving behind the jaded track of the Costa del Sol. The road twisted and turned upwards, past villages sparkling in the winter sun ... *Algarrobo* ... *Frigiliana* ... *Corumbela* ... *Sayalonga,* home of the closed hotel ... *Cómpeta* ... until, finally, at the end of the road, our village: *Canillas de Albaida.* Truly, the end. After our village, you are on your own. You and the mountains. The stacked walls of the *cementerio* on the north face of the village await you if you don't get back in one piece. Looking out on the *Sierras de Almijara, Tejeda y Alhama,* pretenders to the *Sierra Nevada* throne.

As we got closer to our destination, it began to dawn on me just how little time I had spent in the house that Saturday morning. In short, I had liked the feel of it and, there not being a lot of time, I had kept my enquiries to a minimum. Which left me ill-equipped for Helen's questions now that she had nothing else to think of.

The first thing she had asked me when I got home was if there was air conditioning. I had no idea but I swore blind there was. I knew from her tone that this was a deal-breaker. Just as well she didn't ask if the house worked on gas or electricity. As we slowly climbed higher on the gently winding roads, she told me that a garden and a patio were other priorities. I said there was definitely a garden because I had seen one from the roof terrace and it seemed likely that, if there was a garden, there was a patio too. I had to admit that there were gaps in my knowledge.

I wanted to tell her that there wasn't much point in these enquiries at this stage as there was nothing we could do about it and in any event she would have her answers presently. Instead, I sought to distract her by pointing to the almond blossom dotting the mountainside. I was more than a little anxious by the time we got to shaking hands with our landlords.

Reg and Jill were waiting at the bus stop for us and their warm welcome helped to reassure Helen as we crossed the village. On foot. A car would not have got us any closer apparently. When we arrived at the house, Jill offered a guided tour, Reg a whiskey. As the two women disappeared up the stairs I could hear Jill explaining the air conditioning to Helen. First hurdle cleared.

There was a garden alright but it didn't belong to the house. As for the patioing, we would be doing that on the roof. Overall, it wasn't a bad result. Helen was so enchanted by the views from the roof terrace that she had forgotten about the garden and patio. I accepted Reg's offer of a refill.

Including the roof terrace, with its 360-degree views, the building is three-storied. No basement. No matter. We had neither mules nor goats. It stands on a short, six-foot-wide street which has no name. The house beside us is empty; the one opposite, derelict; our patch, private and quiet. At the back, a mimosa casts its shadow over the secret garden that is not ours, where the cat takes its siesta in the afternoon sun.

That first evening we walked the short distance to the *plaza*. Every village has its *plaza*. This one belonged to Franco, *Plaza del Generalissimo*. At least it did until legislation took it off him in 2007, when it was rebranded and given to *Nuestra Señora del Rosario*, Our Lady of the Rosary.

Not much bigger than Centre Court at Wimbledon, the *plaza* slopes down from the seventeenth-century church at one end to the modern town hall at the other. On one side, there is *La Posada*, once a convent, then *Guardia Civil* headquarters, now a hotel; opposite, a restaurant, formerly the town hall, and where the kitchen now is, formerly the prison. There are a few benches, a fountain and lots of flowers, their turn to shine as yet to come that February evening.

For any night of the week, the place was quiet. For a Saturday night, it was deserted. Rodriguez, owner of the hotel, wearing bright green trousers and matching spectacles, greeted us warmly. He led us upstairs to the rustic dining-room with its roaring fire – it can be cold in *Canillas* in February – where the first people we set eyes on were our landlords. No doubt celebrating the rental of their property, as were we. They invited us to join them and, over a pleasant evening, told us the history of the village and how it had changed during the twenty years they had been here.

*   *   *

We slept well in our new home, though we weren't expecting church bells in our bedroom as early as eight. For breakfast we headed to Sergio's, where I had had a hurried coffee four weeks before. We made our way on foot. No choice. No car. All of ten minutes. Five of which were down to the nature of the terrain. Up and down the village goes, up and down the mountain from which it has been carved. We sat in the sunshine with our coffee and minutes later Sergio brought us out a toasted roll with grated tomato, garlic and a drenching of the local olive oil. All was well.

Canillas takes a good photograph. That Sunday morning in early spring sunshine she was at her best. 600 metres above the Mediterranean and 1,400 below the peak of *Maroma*. The village rises from the semi-detached sixteenth-century *Ermita* or Chapel of *San Anton* at the bottom to the *Ermita* of *Santa Ana* at the top. These two *ermitas*, a Roman bridge and the *sierras* are what the village has to offer the visitor. And, of course, the *tranquilidad*.

The picture was complete when, clippety clop, up the main street came the Lone Ranger himself, commanding, as he rode into the fore-court, "Landlord, a glass of your finest." A former polo player, now the owner of the local riding school. For a moment I was in South America. Certainly a long way from the Four Courts in Dublin.

That evening we joined in the local custom of the *paseo*. Instead of turning right outside our hall door for the *plaza*, we turned left. In a matter of minutes, we were on a steep incline past the cemetery and onto a road through the mountains that leads to the *Parque Natural*.

Here, in the olive centre of the world, it was the end of the picking season. There were still some nets to be seen, spread like tablecloths on the ground. The men in the trees shook the branches until the last olives had fallen. The mountain has been terraced and the harvesting has to be done by hand. When the last tree has yielded up the last olive, the farmers fill their silver sacks with the bounty, and pack them into their rickety vans.

As we made our way back, the sun summoned its last rays home and darkness filled the valley below.

* * *

I wondered over that first weekend if we had stumbled on a micro-climate – winter doesn't come to *Canillas* perhaps – until Monday, wet and weary, arrived. A topping of snow on *Maroma* and a message: we hadn't and it does.

Midday, the peace of the village was shattered by the sound of a horn. Till then it was only church bells every fifteen minutes and the crowing of cocks in the *campo*. Traffic is not a problem: there isn't any. What there is, is confined to a sort-of-ring-road around the village. This wasn't any ordinary sounding of a horn. This was a horn that was being leant on, as the Spanish might say, *con entusiasmo*.

"Has to be a wedding", I said knowledgeably. This wasn't my first visit to Spain after all and the Spanish love noise. "I'll go and investigate." Nothing I like better than an adventure. I went around to the church in the *plaza* looking for a bride or at least a groom. The wind-swept, rain-swept square was deserted, the church door bolted. No sign of either.

"Try Angeles in the shop", Helen suggested. I ran down the flight of steps beside our house, anxious not to miss anything.

"*Boda?*" I enquired when I popped my head into her dark shop for the first time. Helen had briefed me. "Wedding?" Whom I took to be Angeles looked blankly at me. Needless to say, the car which was responsible for all of this had moved on so she couldn't know what I was referring to and there was nothing I could point to. The evidence had disappeared.

"*Celebración?*" I was thinking on my feet. And translating. Simultaneously.

"*No*", she replied. "*Todo tranquilo.*" To be fair to her she was doing her best. No *boda* after all.

As I was retracing my steps, the horn resumed. Suspect vehicle returned. Stopping this time. Outside the shop. Driver got out and went around to the rear door, which he opened. As soon as the horn stopped, he started. Roaring. Chanting. Singing out. At the top of his voice. It sounded serious. Had there been a coup in Madrid? As he chanted, he held up a fish, then another until I could make out some of the words – "*gambas* ... *bacalao* ... *cala* ...". The fishmonger was in town. Fresh fish to your door each day. Not a bride in sight. A lap of the village on the horn to begin with and another to do the business.

Angeles emerged from her darkness. She had her own shopping to do. As soon as she saw me, being the business woman she is, she added two and two and let a roar out of her. "*Boda?*" she roared, pointing to the fish man, and burst out laughing. I joined in.

My first *amiga* in *Canillas*.

Our third evening in residence, we tried the village's other restaurant, Paco's, for dinner. When I presented my card at the end of our meal, Jesus, our waiter, indicated that they didn't have a facility for taking cards. To be precise he shook his head.

"*No dinero*", I said in my best Spanish. "Is there a hole in the wall?" He stared blankly at me as his mother, Angeles, had done earlier in the day. Miming a hole and muttering *dinero*, I pointed to the wall, hoping thereby to facilitate understanding. Next.

I held up a ten-Euro note. All I had and, while Paco's prices were reasonable, ten Euro wasn't going to do it. I raised my shoulders and tried to look helpless, which wasn't hard. My intention was to convey an enquiry as to where in the village I might get cash. Something must have got through. He shook his head for a second time.

Only two days in the village and I was insolvent.

At the very least, a liquidity crisis.

"*No problema*", Jesus, who was married to the daughter of the establishment, said. He had never set eyes on us before. "*Mañana*", he continued. "*No problema.*"

My first *amigo* in *Canillas*.

* * *

Tuesday. Day three. Five if you count Malaga.

My novel.

Why I'm here, after all.

No time to lose.

First things first.

Procure a room.

The house has two bedrooms.

"Shall I take the larger one?" I shouted down to Helen.

She wasn't going to be here until July.

The smaller one apparently.

Still, perfect for purpose.

A table – could be bigger – and a chair.

In the corner, an empty bookcase. For my book when it's published.

The walls are white. One window, which looks out on the wall of the house opposite, also white.

A room without a view. No distractions.

A room without a laptop. I couldn't hack cutting and pasting and charging batteries and power shortages and not being in a wifi area and the like. I had a student notebook and black and red pens. For the early drafts. They couldn't disappear into the ether. You couldn't delete them by pressing a button. A portable typewriter, which my brother gave me as a wedding present, for when things got serious. What more could a writer want?

"Mark, I'm only here for a few days. You'll have plenty of time when I'm gone", Helen shouted up the stairs.

*   *   *

I have always hated Ash Wednesday.

Even in Spain. All this fasting, giving up things. Year in, year out. In truth, it must be twenty years since I gave up anything. Just our luck that our first Wednesday in Spain would turn out to be Ash Wednesday.

A friend of mine gives up alcohol for Lent. Which is commendable.

He has a derogation clause however: *Except in an emergency.*

"What constitutes *an emergency?*" a colleague enquired one Lent evening in the bar of the Four Courts.

"When someone invites you for a gin and tonic of course."

In the same spirit I was off alcohol for the day. The whole day. Consecutively.

I went around the village with a long face. It was a long day. The sixth day of my new beginning.

At six, I went to Mass. They don't announce the attendance like they do at football matches so I can't say how many were there. But it was a small crowd. Mainly female, mainly elderly, by which I mean around my age.

Seasonal statues made up the numbers:

Jesus with a crown of thorns.
Jesus with the Cross,
Jesus without the Cross.
Jesus on the Cross, two over-dressed women looking up at Him.
Jesus beneath the Cross.
Jesus in boxers.

Boxers?

No shortage of horror. There should be a sign on the door protecting children.

The ashes were placed on the top of my head rather than on my forehead so I couldn't show them off.

"Didn't you go?" Helen asked when I got back.

"Why do you ask?"

"No ashes."

"They do it differently here. On your head for some reason."

"Cuts out the competition I suppose." Very droll. Only barely hanging in. "Gin and tonic?"

"Of course." Like a bullet from a gun. "It's been a long day."

Delicioso. The tonic
sizzled. Then the ice.
And the lemon from Reg's garden,
as big as a rugby ball.
Forbidden fruit. The fun,
in breaking the rules, after all.

* * *

That was it. Ash Wednesday done and dusted for another year. And all that giving up stuff. As if in harmony, the snow on Maroma melted. Now for Valentine's Day, which I wasn't expecting in Spain.

Jill had invited Helen to a special Valentine's Day coffee morning. To introduce her.

"How did it go?" I asked when she got back.

"Lovely. Nice people. Very welcoming."

"Any foreigners?"

"When you say foreigners?"

"Spanish. People who don't speak English."

"One spoke Irish."

"What?"

"Cork."

"The whole way out here to meet a woman from Cork?"

"To answer your question, we all speak English. They're dying to meet you."

"Why on earth?"

"I told them you're a writer, you're out here writing a novel and you have a deadline."

"A deadline?"

"Sounds better. Less of the aspirational about it."

I know I went public in Portugal. But to announce to her coffee morning in our first week that I am a writer and that I have a deadline was pushing it a bit.

"They have a book club too and they'd like you to speak to them."

"Me? About what?"

"Writing, of course."

"But I haven't written anything."

I shouldn't let her out. Is it Rigoletto who locks up his daughter?

Restauranteur Paco wasn't the only Paco in the village. Jill wanted us to meet another, Paco 2, the village postman. He is about ten and opens his office three hours later for half an hour each day. It's a small village. A one-bar electric fire warms his office.

"Paco, meet Helen and Mark."

"*Encantado*", Paco responded charmingly.

"*Hola Paco*", we said back. Faultless Spanish. I felt like patting him on the head and telling him they're smashing shoes he's wearing. Paco smiled and said something. Probably along the lines of "What can I do for you?" He seemed an obliging sort of chap. Jill explained that she wanted to know the address of her house – the one we were renting. Jill didn't have very good Spanish. Paco looked puzzled. "You want to know the address of your house?"

This was a sub-plot of our making: There is a number on the white-washed wall of our house but we couldn't make out if it is a seven or a curly number one. This isn't a matter of huge importance but on balance we think that if post is coming all the way from Ireland that it should bear the correct address. We had raised the matter at local level – Jill – and now Jill was raising it at official level – Paco 2 – on our behalf.

Paco 2 could have said it didn't make a blind bit of difference as there are only two other houses on our street, one unoccupied, the other derelict. He didn't say anything of the sort.

As we were tossing the matter forwards or backwards, it occurred to me that if there are only three houses, how can one of them be number seven: he had enough on his plate.

Full credit to him. He understood immediately and acted decisively. No humming. Less hawing. No bureaucracy.

"You can have whichever number you like", he said with a flourish, "curly one or seven. I couldn't give a toss."

Pleased with himself, we turned to the main item on the agenda.

"Helen and Mark will be living here for a while. Please deliver their post to our house", Jill said in her halting – almost stationary – Spanish.

"But that's not your house." Paco 2 looked puzzled for a second time in as many minutes. His look of puzzlement like Angeles' blank stare earlier in the week. Perhaps a *Canillas* thing.

"What do you mean, it's not our house", she asked him a little crossly. It had been her house for ten years. She was entitled to be a little crossly.

"Your house is in *el campo*", said Paco.

"I know where my house is thank you Paco. I have two houses, one in the *pueblo* and one in the *campo*. Helen and her husband will be staying in the *pueblo* and they would like their post to be delivered there."

"Why didn't you say that at the beginning?" asked Paco, whose English was improving with the practice.

"I did say it", said Jill. "You mis ... oh forget it."

Reg, who had wisely stayed out of the discussion, decided it was time to put points on the board.

"It's probably the heat darling", he said ridiculously, in an attempt to calm matters. "I think Paco has got the message."

"Stay out of it Reg. You've done quite well up to now. How could it be the heat? It's February." She had a point. The meeting with Paco had gone way over schedule and ended abruptly, which was probably just as well.

We got our post alright. Along with Jill's and Reg's. For a few weeks – until that too was sorted.

Prompted by the fact that it was Valentine's Day, I took Helen back to Rodriguez's for a romantic dinner. We got romance alright. Cupids and balloons and soft music. Rodriguez even lit a candle. One. We had the restaurant to ourselves.

"We'll have the Valentine's Day menu please Rodriguez", I mimed. Rodriguez was in red today. Red trousers, red glasses. The occasion, if not the menu.

"You can't", he said.

"Why not?" I asked.

"It's not on today."

"But it's Valentine's Day."

"I know but the Valentine's Day menu is for the weekend."

"What?"

We were long enough married not to be put out by a setback like this. I had thought that black pudding was a Clonakilty thing but it's a specialty here also. I ordered it to start, followed by the wild boar and the most expensive wine on the list, a *Ribero del Duero* called *Delirio* which was *delicioso*. Helen had *gambas pil-pil*, sizzling prawns, and *solomillo de cerdo*, fillet of pork. It wasn't long before we had put our disappointment over the menu behind us. A *chupito* on the way out, Rodriguez on his red knees with a flower for Helen and all was forgiven.

* * *

There was an urgent message from Helen's boss when we got back from the restaurant. Could she return early? Something had come up and she needed Helen for the weekend. She only had to ask – Helen was that sort of person. She was lucky to get the last seat on the only plane the following day.

The bus got us to the airport with no time to spare. Which was probably just as well. Helen didn't do tears but, on this occasion, I felt they weren't far away. As we parted, I mentioned my birthday and said that I hoped she might come out for it. A kiss and a final wave and she was gone.

I headed into Malaga for a late lunch. On my own. I had better get used to it.

I had been given precisely what I had asked for.

Time and space.

The opportunity to write.

I had thought of this often.

Never believing it could happen.

According to Helen,

I had gone on about it.

Now here it was

On a plate before me.

Suddenly,

For the first time

In this chapter,

I was nervous.

Could I deliver? Was I kidding myself? Walter Mitty? Sticking to the middle lane all my life, was I going to make a fool of myself now? Definitely, I was experiencing a deficit in the endorphins department.

I found a smart and busy *tapas* bar off *Calle Larios* in Malaga. On a high stool at the counter in a multi-coloured, short-sleeved shirt and shorts, surrounded by well-dressed men on a lunch break from

their offices, I was pretty conspicuous if anyone cared to look. The
animated conversations around me intensified my introspection.

What was I doing here on my own, in this packed bar in Malaga,
on a Friday in February? I should be at my lunch table in the Four
Courts. Discussing who had said what in court that morning. Who
would be sleeping with whom later that night. Whether or not Ireland
could lift another Grand Slam.

When I arrived in the bar, the mirror behind the counter was full of
the suits surrounding me, chatting noisily and waving their hands. After
a while, lunch break over, the mirror emptied until only the barman
and I were left. He looking at me, and me looking at him looking at
me. Hopper in Spain. I wanted to talk to the barman. I had to talk to
someone. Helen's plane had not even left the ground, and already I
needed company.

Forget the writing – how was I going to survive without her? Six
months. We had never been separated for that long. Solitude sounds
great in a crowded room. Had I thought this thing through at all?
Would I end up talking to a white-washed wall? How could I integrate
with the villagers? They were very pleasant and welcoming but there's
only so much *hola*-ing you can do.

As for the kitchen? How was I going to feed myself for the next six
months? I couldn't have pancakes every night. I can't cook. I never had
to. I did my work and little else. Helen did hers and everything else.

"Are you enjoying your holiday?" enquired the barman. Fair
enough, it was a reasonable shot given the shirt and shorts.

"I'm not on holiday actually. I'm writing a book, a novel." I couldn't
believe it was me saying this. So matter of factly.

"Lucky you. I'd love to be able to do that." Perfect English.

"Write a novel?"

"No. Paint. Paint full-time. It's all I've ever wanted to do. But I can't
afford that of course. My parents have given up on me. You have
to have a career they say. To fall back on. Mother from Scotland.
Voted NO in the Referendum. Father, lawyer in Madrid." Lawyers
everywhere.

"That's a coincidence. So am I. In Dublin. Your dad is right you
know." I couldn't help it.

"That's what everyone says. No risks. I'll probably end up doing what he says. For the moment, I've dropped out. Three days a week here to pay the rent and four days in the mountains painting. That's mine there. José lets me hang it."

I turned around and studied his painting. It wasn't immediately obvious what it was but the colours were vibrant.

"I like it", I said. The young man's enthusiasm was cheering me up.

"Thanks. Who knows? Maybe someone will come in and discover me. What about your novel?"

"Oh, early days. Only here a week. Just dropped my wife to the airport. Back to the village this evening. Work starts in earnest tomorrow."

"What's it about or can you say?"

"Don't know."

"That's exciting. I have friends who are writers. I've heard them say that. They don't know what they're going to write from day to day. Apparently it's liberating."

"It's liberating alright. It's downright scary. All my life has been about preparation. You don't go into court with a blank page. Ask your father. Not sure if I can handle it. Will you excuse me? Bus to catch. You've cheered me up. I was beginning to feel a bit lonely."

"I could see that."

"And to doubt what I am about to do."

"Doubt is part of it."

"Good luck with the painting."

"Here we say *buena suerte.*"

"Very well. *Buena suerte. Adiós.*" A confident young man, at the other end of life.

"*Adiós amigo.*"

Why hadn't I encouraged him, I thought to myself as I walked along *Avenida de los Artistas*?

I wasn't hungry when I got home. I had made a meal of the *tapas*. Something light. Helen had shown me how to rustle up a few things. Just in case. Pancakes were one of them. Together on Shrove Tuesday, while the party was getting underway in Rio, we had rustled up a fine pancake. Slim and weightless, drenching it in the juice of Reg's lemons. We had even taken a picture. Nothing to it. I had seen Master Chefs do it in a jiffy with great ease. I set to.

The first thing was to identify the white of egg. I phoned home. Then I whipped the mixture in a large bowl. So far, according to plan. Pour the liquid mixture onto the frying pan. Easy peasy. I had seen it on the telly. The mixture flows onto the pan like a waterfall. Not mine. Mine had become a solid mass the size of a football and was refusing to leave the bowl. I gave it a few slaps and it plopped out.

Eventually.

It didn't come within an ass's roar of the template. What had happened between Shrove Tuesday and Friday and why was I surprised? The only thing to do was put it on Facebook. My first attempt at cooking in Spain, six months to go.

"Rome wasn't built in a day", my wife said when I phoned her to say goodnight. I don't know why, but in Spanish it's Rome wasn't built in two days. Kind, but what had Rome got to do with it?

* * *

The first thing I did when I woke was to let in the sun and hopefully a good dollop of inspiration. Then I brought my breakfast onto the roof and timed the sun's assault on *Maroma*. They weren't breakfasting on roof-tops in Dublin on a Saturday morning in February. I had pencilled in Monday for resumption of my writing career and I thought I would spend the weekend familiarising myself with the house and the village, possibly throwing in a few household chores.

I had just hung up my socks on the line on the roof when I heard "*Hola*" from higher up. An elderly Spanish woman I had never seen before. I *hola*-ed back. She couldn't leave it at that. I smiled a lot and waved and kept repeating "*gracias.*" After a while, she moved on but only to another topic. One word I could make out was "*vino*" as she mimed pouring a glass of wine down her throat. Eventually I said "*gracias*" for the last time and went downstairs.

A few minutes later the doorbell rang. The same elderly Spanish woman stood there, with a large plastic container. She was very friendly and invited herself in. I thought as a matter of decorum I should leave the door open. She closed it. I offered her a teabag. She pointed to the container. *Vino.* Local brew. Hers. I poured two of the smallest glasses I could find – it was eleven in the morning – and we sat sipping. She kept repeating *"bueno?"* I kept repeating *"si, gracias."* I wasn't sure how long this could go on. She had no such difficulty. She seemed to think that the more quickly she spoke the more likely I was to understand. Her voice dropped and I sensed something more intimate:

How long are you here for?

Do you own the house?

Are you renting?

Who owns it?

In the silences in the aftermath of her questions, I decided the best course was to pretend I couldn't understand her. Which I couldn't. I could barely hear her. Finally, as the landlady arrived,

How much is the rent?

"Qué pasa?" said Jill, her Spanish improving, as I waved her in. Within seconds, *Señora* was gone, container of wine, lighter by two small glasses, between her legs.

"What did she want?" Jill wanted to know.

"I think she was selling her wine but we hadn't got that far."

"And having a good snoop. They're always trying to get inside your door. Say nothing. That's my advice."

"Whatever you say landlord."

"Really, you should have more sense", Jill said.

Jill was on a mission of hospitality, much like my neighbour, and I was delighted to accept her invitation to dinner on Sunday evening. All the more so given my efforts of the night before.

END OF MONTH REPORT

Word Count: Still Zero

New Spanish Phrase Learnt by Heart: *Dónde esta el cajero?* [Where is the ATM?]

Own Meals Prepared and Cooked: One, a Disaster

4

MARCH

Day 1 of Writing

Monday morning. One week gone by. Not to mention forty years. And a weekend if you want to be pedantic. Time to get started. I wasn't here to enjoy myself or play golf. I was on a mission. No time to be lost. Anyway, the book club could be looking for me and I had better be started at least if I was going to address them. I had no excuse now that I was on my own. How often over the years had I wanted to give it a go at home but, always, there were things to be done? I was finding out that if I insist on doing *everything I have to do* before sitting down to write, I will never write. At last, here I was with nothing between me and a good night's sleep. Except a pancake of course. It had even begun to rain.

Room ready, what next? I asked myself. There was no one else to ask. How do I start? Millions of them out there. Everyone was at it.

Bookshops packed with books. Each starting with a blank page. We had that in common. Do you think first and write later? Or, write first and see what happens? These were novel questions.

Danny had bought me a book. A going-away-to-write present. A book on how to write a book. He had even inscribed it,
"For my friend,
May you write your dream, *hombre*.
See you in a year.
Danny."

I opened it.
Chapter 1:
Get up, it said.
Write
From 9 to 1
Mobile off.
Write
From 2 to 6
Mobile off.
Seven days a week.
Terrifying.
2,000 words a day,
Even more terrifying.
(definite and indefinite articles not included)
I took out an *Irish Times* and counted two thousand words.
Every day?

Dylan Thomas's wife locked him into the garden shed, but I'm not sure it had anything to do with writing.

The man in the street will tell you to write about what you know. "*Write about what you know*", he'll say. Knowingly. The book says the same. I should know something about being a barrister – after forty years. But what about the poet from Paraguay? Was it Paraguay? What did he say? I hadn't even begun and there were issues. In a nutshell:
To write or not to write
about what I know

or what I don't?

Maybe the parrot from Paraguay was referring to poetry.

How was I going to make this decision? Probably a good idea to thrash it out on the phone that evening with Helen.

In the meantime, reading on, the book devotes an entire chapter to PLOT. Work out your plot before writing a word, it insists.

Always one to heed advice, I sat back in the chair, hands behind my head, and started to work out my plot. Opting for what I know about for the moment. What about a plot where

a barrister murders someone,

murders a judge perhaps,

or a solicitor

or is himself murdered?

The public loves a good murder

or a political scandal plot?

And sex of course.

Lots of sex.

As I plotted, I doodled. The page filled with doodles. No sign of a plot. But then that's what the book says ... Plot ... Plot ... Plot ... though it doesn't mention doodles. I was getting tired. All this plotting, doodling. How long was I to spend working out my plot? Important not to overdo it. Another thing the book says.

"Is it finished?" Sergio asked as I ordered my drink. How could it be finished? I'm only here a week. Anyway, how did he know? I didn't bother responding.

The bar was packed. Malaga, local team, just down the road, well 56 km down the road, at home to Man. United. 2-1 to Malaga in the second half. The audience was on its feet with the exception of two gentlemen in the corner from the north of England. M.U. fans of course.

"Pretty shitty", one said to the other in his northern accent, looking out the window. What did he expect in February? And if it was "pretty shitty" here, it was likely to be pretty shittier wherever he came from. Perhaps he was talking about the football.

The football and the pints had done me good and I went home feeling sharp and looking forward to my second day as a writer. I even jotted down a few ideas that had come to me during the match. Writers do that. Desk at nine. On the dot.

In the meantime, I thought I'd ring Helen. Progress report. She'd like that. Clear up that what-to-write-about thing.

"Darling, is that you?"

"Who do you think it is? Julia Roberts? What time is it?"

Rather a lot of questions.

Not like Helen to be cross.

"Usually you like me ringing."

"Not at one in the morning."

"It couldn't be one, could it?"

"No, you're right, it's two where you are."

"I just went up to Sergio's for a drink and watch the football. Malaga won."

"Did you ring me to tell me that?"

"No, in fact I didn't. I rang you to discuss the book. Just something I wanted to run by you."

"Not at two in the morning."

"It's only one where you are."

"Eh, Mark ...".

"OK. OK. Goodnight. Phone you tomorrow."

"When hopefully you will be in better form", I added after I had put the phone down.

Not a good idea, the phone call.

* * *

DAY 2 OF WRITING

Woke at eleven. Altitude I suppose. Still unwinding after forty years of rising at dawn. Alarm clock needed. All set to start at two when post arrived. For Jill and Reg. From the UK. "Very Urgent." Better deliver it immediately and mention it to Paco 2 if he's still there.

Their *campo* residence is on the road to *Archez*, a Moorish village which opposed Franco in the Civil War. As a career move, not a great one. No sign of Paco 2. The road descends steeply. Around here, everything is steeply. Either up or down, steeply. No half-way house, no level playing pitch. Past the swimming pool on the right and the semi-detached *ermita* on the left. Oranges sparkling in the trees like Christmas lights. Olive and avocado trees filling the terraces. Post delivered, I carried on down to *Archez*. It was too nice to be indoors and it was a chance to explore our nearest neighbour.

The spotless village is smaller than *Canillas* and more deserted, if that is possible. A weekly market was taking place outside another spanking new *Ayuntamiento*. There were houses for rent, houses for sale. There was even a tourist office. If I had thought Paco 2 had it easy, the bank in *Archez* opens for an hour a week. I asked a youngster for the time and she asked for a cigarette. A Muslim woman offered to show me the fifteenth-century minaret, the pride of the village.

I was sitting outside the only bar in the village having a glass of wine and some olives when a man sat down with a pint and started to talk. To me, presumably, as there was no one else around.

"I had a row with the wife last night", he said. "She wants to go back to England."

Entirely a matter for her, I thought to myself. I don't care.

"I like it here. Never want to set foot on English soil again."

Entirely a matter for him. I still don't care.

"You never know what's going on in a woman's head", he said, broadening the discussion.

"I agree with you there." He was in need of support.

"She can go as far as I'm concerned."

He went instead and another took his place.

"Don't pay the slightest attention to what he told you", the replacement said. "They get on well enough. She will never leave him and it would help if he drank less."

I thanked the replacement and left. A steep climb to an empty house. I couldn't wait to get to the desk.

I had heard it said that even when writers aren't writing their brains are ticking over. Like crows, picking at ideas and words. Deep in the basement of the imagination the story is bubbling away. Something like this must have been happening to me on the road to *Archez*. Or, on the road back. By bedtime I had sorted the plot thing. I would write about a barrister starting out at the Bar. That I knew about. To hell with Helen and the poet from Paraguay. Or was it Patagonia?

* * *

Day 3 of Writing

Dawn.

Jumped out of bed.

Full of the joys of being a writer.

Only at it two days. One really. Two big decisions made. I would write about what I knew and I had sorted my plot. In an outline sort of way. My book would be about a young barrister starting out. All that was left was the writing bit. According to Danny's book, the hard work done. Like an essay at school, the key, a plan. Once you had that you were sailing. Without it, very quickly, you were at sea. I tore up the plotless page full of doodles and took another blank page.

Now for the opening line, the reader's first encounter with the writer. According to the book, very important. Only one chance to make a first impression. I took down some of Helen's books – Helen is a great reader – and looked at their opening lines. You couldn't expect to write a novel without doing research.

"It was the horse that brought me to Spain", is how Penelope Chetwode opens *Two Middle-Aged Ladies in Andalusia*, a story set in the early sixties. The ladies in question are Penelope herself, aged 51, and *La Marquesa*, a middle-aged horse belonging to the Duke of Wellington. Chetwode rides *La Marquesa* around *Andalucía* for a month recording her experiences.

Not bad.

"riverrun, past Eve and Adam's, from swerve of shore to bend of bay, brings us by a commodius vicus of recirculation back to Howth Castle and Environs."

Don't think so.

By lunchtime, I had the idea, page full of opening lines.

By mid-afternoon, there was a line through all of them. I was becoming impatient. If the opening line was taking this long, how long would the book take? The Christmas market was less than nine months away. Perhaps I was developing writer's block.

What I was certainly developing was tiredness and a pain in my knee. Had I overdone it on the road to *Archez*? I took myself upstairs to bed and fell asleep. When I awoke three hours later, the pain was worse and my knee had swollen. After Monday night I was reluctant to ring Helen. However, she's good at this sort of thing. Doctor's daughter after all. Hopefully, she'd forgotten the other night.

"I'll fly out immediately", she said.

"That won't be necessary", I replied. "Maybe tomorrow."

Confident that a few glasses of wine or a bottle might do the trick, I headed for the *plaza*. Walking was excruciating, getting my leg up the two steps into the bar a nightmare, up the stairs to the restaurant out of the question. I sat at the counter and made my way through the bottle. The few glasses would never have done it. When I was leaving, Rodriguez, yellow trousers, yellow glasses, gave me a walking stick and his mobile number. Crossing the *plaza* took as long as the opening line. I reached home eventually. The whole ordeal had taken so long that the wine had worn off and I was left with a long night.

Much as I was in need of sympathy, I wasn't going there.

* * *

What Should Have Been Day 4 of Writing

I didn't think the pain could get worse. In the morning, I had to come down the stairs on my arse. There was nothing for it but to find a doctor. Where might he be? And where might that be? At the furthest point of the village. Between the bus terminus and a shrine to *Nuestra Señora del Rosario. Señora* is everywhere. I joined the queue. The queue in the health centre. The doctor reached me just as it was time for *desayuno*, their word for breakfast but, at eleven o'clock, more likely to be elevenses. The world stops for *desayuno*. Off he went with his assistant and his nurse, without a word. Unfortunately, *desayuno* did nothing for his bedside manner, which was sadly lacking. He was a dour gentleman, the doctor.

I did feel that he knew what he was at, though I didn't understand a word he said. Whether he was unable to speak English or refused to, I couldn't decide. He despatched me with a letter to a hospital in *Torre del Mar*, a town, not surprisingly, on the coast. He had no interest in how I was getting there and I didn't bother asking him.

I may have been at the terminus but the same could not be said of the bus, which was not due until 3.30. A *deus ex machina* was called for and arrived in the form of a small Spanish gentleman smoking a cigar.

"*Que tal?*" he asked

"*Muy mal*", I said, pointing to my knee. I could barely walk

He too had been to the doctor, he said, and threw his eyes up to heaven.

"Hospital", I muttered.

"Taxi?" he muttered back.

"You're on."

Within minutes we were hurtling down the road towards *Archez* for my second time in three days. Pablo was keen to agree the fare. I was in no mood for haggling.

"Sixty", he said.

"Sixty", I said.

"Fifty", he thought I said.

We were not *ad idem* as far as Pablo was concerned, so he called for another round of negotiations. Due to the language difficulties, the going was slow to non-existent. He started to fooster in the glove compartment with his right hand while continuing to steer with his left. His foostering hand returned after a few bends with the stub of a pencil and a bit of paper. As the road twisted and narrowed and the drop on either side came into play, Pablo started to write. It wasn't easy, driving and writing and smoking your cigar. It wasn't easy, watching. Eventually I made out the figures six and zero and realised what he was at. "*Si, si, si ...*" I roared a hundred times. Had there been a one in front of the sixty I would have roared "*si*" too. Pablo was happy at last and we carried on towards the sea.

There was a "*no fumar*" sign on the dashboard. Pablo whistled for a while and then resumed the chat. It flowed easily from him until he thought that I thought that he had said he was seventy when in fact he had said he was eighty and the pencil and paper had to come out again. It was a relief to reach the hospital.

Not for long.

My European Health Card was out of date.

As if I didn't have enough on my knee. I rang Helen.

"Nonsense", she said. "It isn't and there isn't a problem." Helen could be a bit dismissive.

There may not have been a problem for her at the top of the queue in the Blackrock Shopping Centre in Dublin. There sure was a problem for me at the top of the queue at hospital reception in *Torre del Mar*.

"For heaven's sake, don't put up with any of that bureaucratic nonsense. You know what they're like."

I repeated all of this – less the nonsense bit – to the Spanish receptionist looking after me. To no effect. To be fair, on the face of it, she was on the right side of the argument. My immediate future hung in the balance. I had the distinct impression that I was about to be thrown out when a Venezuelan lady stepped in. From Venezuela. She was a volunteer interpreter in the hospital and spoke better English than I. Spanish, her native tongue. Apparently Spanish is spoken widely in South America. She took over the discussion. Minutes later, I was being wheeled into A+E by a triumphant Pablo, my guardian angel, still puffing.

In no time at all (three hours and fifty-eight minutes to be precise) I was introduced to the orthopaedic surgeon. I couldn't believe it. He just had to be the brother of the doctor in *Canillas*. He read the letter and examined me. He informed me through the lady that I had liquid on the knee.

"Probably alcohol", I said, not knowing how I managed humour in all the circumstances.

The good doctor wasn't possessed of a sense of humour. Definitely the brother.

"They're going to drain it", the lady all-the-way-from-Venezuela said. I didn't like the sound of this.

I was trying to work out where Venezuela is on the map. I didn't do geography at school. I know it's South America. I know roughly the shape of South America. But where in South America? I wanted to tell the nice lady that my grandmother was from Buenos Aires. Obviously she wouldn't know her – she is much younger – but I thought that it might help to cement our relationship if Argentina borders Venezuela and she knew that my grandmother had been born right beside her. If Argentina doesn't border Venezuela, the exercise is a complete waste of time.

"Tell him I'm not a happy bunny", I said to the lady-from-Venezuela. All I was looking for was a bit of sympathy.

He asked her if I wanted to go, which I thought was uncalled for. I said that in view of the fact that he was going to operate I would like to phone my wife. He said it wasn't an operation and a phone call wouldn't be necessary. I hadn't said it was necessary, merely that I'd like to. Lost in translation.

To be fair to him (why?), more than likely this wasn't his only drainage of the day and he was keen to proceed to other drainages. Loved his work. Each time the needle approached, I froze like a virgin and withdrew my knee. After a few false starts he said that if I did it a third time I would be disqualified. I took that as an ultimatum and knuckled down. As the needle penetrated the skin I wondered if the Spanish word for ultimatum is *ultimatumo*.

We were done. *Medico* Brothers 2 – Me 0. The attendant was wheeling me to San Pablo's taxi. On the way out, I asked for a comment card but they were out of them. I was given a prescription instead and told to return to my health centre on Monday. When we reached *Canillas* the *farmacia* was closed. Couldn't face the two steps into Rodriguez. Another long night lay ahead.

* * *

Arrived at *farmacia* one hour before opening. What clown puts a chemist at the top of a flight of steps? I took the first anti-inflammatory at one minute after nine and at one minute after ten it began to kick in. What a relief to be out of pain and to be able to walk normally. I celebrated that evening by returning Rodriguez's stick and taking the stairs to his restaurant two at a time.

* * *

Monday morning, I returned to the health centre as instructed.

It was a joy to be able to cross the sleepy, steeply up-and-down village with a normal gait. As I made the journey, I wondered if there was any chance that he had died over the weekend. I couldn't believe my luck. A female doctor. I scanned the walls for a death notice. I could hardly ask straight out.

It was a joy to talk to her. Even though she was telling me that I would have to inject myself daily for ten days. Inject myself? I explained with intense grimacing that I didn't care for injections and certainly couldn't inject myself. Very kindly, she told me to come back the following day and she'd do it.

* * *

I did.

She didn't.

She wasn't even there.

There had been a resurrection. He was back. If anything, fuller of life. Shouting *cita* at me. Whatever it meant, it wasn't friendly. He wasn't going to see me. That much was clear. As a final throw of the dice, I showed him my box of needles. He went for his *desayuno*.

On the way out, I asked for a comment card.

I went home, upstairs to my bedroom, and, there being no alternative, spread the equipment on the bed:

top-of-the-range needles from top-of-the steps *farmacia;*

alcohol and balls of cotton wool from Angeles – she was most sympathetic when I told her the full story but she did have a shop to run;

a bottle of brandy by way of consolation.

The theory was simple:

1. Dip cotton wool in alcohol and apply to stomach;
2. Grab chunk of stomach – no shortage – and hold tightly in left hand;
3. Take needle in right hand and bring into contact with chunk;
4. Take deep breath and insert;
5. Press down on needle with right thumb so that fluid is released into chunk;

6.   When all fluid has been released, withdraw needle;
7.   Dab injected area with cotton wool soaked in alcohol;
8.   Breathe out while pouring medicinal brandy.

An hour later I was still at it. I could manage 1 and 2. The stumbling block was number 3. Take needle in right hand and *bring into contact with chunk*. Numbers 4 and 5 would be difficult too.

Surely, in the twenty-first century, there is an easier way.

I tried bigger chunks; I tried squeezing bigger chunks tighter; I even tried hiding the needle in a basketball of cotton wool, pretending it wasn't there.

Heroism was called for:

I remembered the first day my swimming instructor, on whom I had a crush, put me into the Big Pool in the Swimming Baths at Blackrock on the south side of Dublin. I was ten years of age. She was big too and had a pole. The *idea* was that I would spring lightly, first into the air and then the water, at the same time grabbing the pole. Heroism was nowhere to be found. My instructor had retired before I left the steps.

I remembered the first time I swallowed a raw egg. Part of a fitness regime. It was about two years after the Big Pool and I was mad about sport at the time. I took it out into the garden to have it *al fresco*. Which was optional. I hoped that the pretty girl next door might see me and be impressed and I might go up her ladder. I popped the raw egg, less the shell, into my mouth and moved it around with my tongue. It was a fair fit. I wouldn't have been able to get a second one in. The swallow was the next thing. I was getting ready when I remembered I already had an apple down there. Would there be room for a passing egg? What if I choked? In the end, I wasn't that dedicated either to my sport or the girl next door.

Conclusion: when it came to heroism, I had no precedent to call upon.

It was getting dark. I closed my eyes, uttered an ejaculation and did the business. I poured myself a bottle of brandy and breathed a sigh of life.

*   *   *

Nine days of abuse later, I had finished the needles and the brandy. Still the saga continued.

I was better and wanted the doctor to confirm. I needed an appointment. *CITA*. That was what he had been trying to tell me all along. Why I couldn't make an appointment in the health centre in *Canillas*, I had no idea. I had to go to the health centre in *Algarrobo*. Halfway to Malaga. Further by bus. Apparently, Jaime is the *hombre*. He would look after me.

No one told me that he only works mornings so when I boarded the afternoon bus to *Algarrobo* I was already too late.

No one told me that the following day was *Día de Andalucía*, a public holiday, so when I boarded the morning bus I was on another wasted journey. Health centre closed.

When I eventually got to Jaime, he was very understanding but his understanding fell short of an appointment. He insisted on a current European Health Card. One that had expired two years previously was of no interest to him. In that sense he was a stickler. No flair. No flexibility. His hands were tied, he said. They seemed perfect to me. Helen had rung me the night before to say that she was coming out for my birthday. I told him this. It didn't add anything. A game-changer for most, Helen turning up. Not our Jaime.

Lashing here. Fed up with the weather. It had been raining for the entire of this ordeal. All the locals could say was that it was needed in the *campo*. Fed up with my knee and Spanish bureaucracy. All I wanted was a final appointment with the doctor and goodbye.

Instead, I lost my credit card.

Mist came down *Maroma* like an invading army, storming the village ... taking the heath centre, doctor inside, and Jaime with it.

Andalucía gets 333 days of sunshine a year. Not this year, sunshine.

* * *

**WHEN I GET OLDER LOSING MY HAIR
MANY YEARS FROM NOW
WILL YOU STILL BE SENDING ME A VALENTINE**

BIRTHDAY GREETINGS, BOTTLE OF WINE?
IF I'D BEEN OUT TILL QUARTER TO THREE
WOULD YOU LOCK THE DOOR?
Will YOU STILL NEED ME, WILL YOU STILL FEED ME
WHEN I'M SIXTY-FOUR?

Today is the day. 64. All the way from that first dance. Can I believe it? Milestone. Millstone. *Feliz Cumpleaños*. Do The Beatles care?

Helen arrived with European Health Card. Current.

"You've lost weight", her first words.

"I wonder why", I replied, giving her a big kiss.

Break the bus journey from airport to village to call into Jaime in *Algarrobo*.

"*Encantado*", said Jaime when I introduced him to Helen.

"*Estupendo*", said Jaime when Helen handed him the Book of Kells. A day for words beginning with '*E*', obviously.

Jaime didn't even look at it and gave me a *cita* for the afternoon.

Back I went, three on the dot, waving my *cita*. No shouting. No *merienda*, afternoon tea. Like a puppy, the doctor examined my knee, patted it and, to my astonishment, "Is there anything else bothering you my friend?" in perfect English. I was on the point of mentioning post-traumatic stress disorder but settled for the inside of my mouth, where I thought I was developing a stress-related abscess.

"Do you think I'm a dentist?" he roared. But only in my imagination. He looked in my mouth, prescribed an antibiotic and said *adiós*.

I am now exempt from medical service for the rest of my life.

"What was all the fuss?" Helen asked as we left. "He seems perfectly charming."

I didn't engage. Tossed the comment card into recycling instead.

Freed from the tyranny of taking liquid out and putting liquid in, I gladly accepted Helen's invitation to **BIRTHDAY GREETINGS, BOTTLE OF WINE**. You aren't 64 every day of the week.

And, wasn't I here writing my novel? Writing the dream, *hombre*. Not that there had been much of that during the *rodilla* episode.

* * *

Day 4 of Writing

After a promising start –
    getting the room ready,
    working out the plot
    embarking on the opening line –
the novel had gone on the back-burner for obvious reasons. I am
not one to shy away from hard work nor yield to adversity. *Bring it on,*
I say. But there are limits. There are times when you have to accept that
your *best-laid schemes* have been well and truly shafted or *ganged
aft agley.* Can't stand Robbie Burns. Surgery was one of them.

I didn't ask for *liquida* on my *rodilla.* It happened. It wasn't my
fault. Nor was it my fault that it took almost three weeks to recover
and be discharged. How was I to know Jaime didn't work afternoons
and that the health centre in *Algarrobo* would be closed on *Día de
Andalucía*?

I had lost three weeks, give or take. Plus the time before. Over
a month. Eleven left. There was only one thing for it. Back up on the
horse. Someone somewhere once said "it doesn't matter if you fall off
seven times as long as you get back up eight." Probably a mathema-
tician. I'm not aware if significance attaches to the numbers seven or
eight or, for example, could you, without distortion, substitute seven-
teen and eighteen. Provided of course you substitute in that order and
not vice versa.

Anyway, like the warrior I am, I was back in the white room at
nine on Monday morning. Raring to go. My mind had not been idle
during my absence. I had been thinking about that elusive opening
line. According to the book, it is important to engage the reader immediately. Obvious really. Bring him in. Neither too startling nor bland.
Just the right mix to make him want to read on. I knew a girl in university who was doing her literature doctorate on opening lines of novels.
Wonder what the opening line of her doctorate was. Unfortunately,
that was forty-five years ago and we hadn't kept in touch.

When I first met Arnold I was in my second year at the Bar
was what I had come up with. I set it down. Read it aloud a few
times. It sounded good and read well. Had immediacy. It introduced

Arnold from what is now hideously called the *get-go*, informed the reader that I was a barrister, but only a starting up one, and suggested that Arnold and I would become an item. I read it aloud again:

When I first met Arnold I was in my second year at the Bar.

Each time it got better. I'm not saying it's *Wuthering Heights* or *Catcher in the Rye*, but it rolled easily off the tongue. The first words I had written since my short story at university. I was pleased. I called Helen.

She was very good. Rose to the occasion.

"Super", she said as if she had just finished *Gone with the Wind*.

I was over the moon and suggested we go to the *plaza* for lunch. It was lovely. The sun was shining. *Tapas* and too much wine, delightful. It was only the first line but it dominated our conversation. Only fourteen words, counting two *I*s, but I felt I was on the road. By the time we got back all I was fit for was a *siesta*.

The following day I accompanied Helen to the airport. By lunchtime I was on my own again. Less the introspection that marked the previous occasion. I headed for my *tapas* bar and my painter friend. Bar packed like the last time but no sign of friend. Eventually got to talk to guy who looked like the boss.

"*Por favor* ... *Señor* ... a few weeks ago ... pointing to the past ... me here ... and *amigo* ... pointing to behind the bar ... painter ... miming painting ... *dónde mi amigo?*"

"*Qué?*" Not surprisingly, in this bar packed with lunchtime trade, I didn't have the guy's exclusive attention. As he was listening to me, he was pouring wine, serving *tapas* and feeling the *camarera*'s bottom.

I had another go.

"*Ah, amigo*", he said as if the way *he* said it made all the difference. "*Si, si.*"

"*Si, si,* what?" Clearly, he hadn't grasped that I was asking a question. "*Amigo dónde?*"

"*Ah, dónde?*" We were off again. There was obviously something about my Spanish that he just wasn't getting.

"*Si, dónde?*"

"*No sé.*"

I gave up.

There is a limit to what can be expected of one in the matter of maintaining a friendship. The bar next door was empty and I had a solitary *menu del día* there.

* * *

I was delighted Helen came out. Birthday and all that. While I loved my village, I was lonely without her. And of course she fixed up the *rodilla* issue by bringing the health card. And managed to put a few meals in the freezer for me. The pancake had been a disaster and resulted in a loss of confidence. So I had begun to eat out. Every night. The village restaurants are lovely. If you are living on your own, it is good to get out. You can't be holed up in a house all day, every day. Any doctor will tell you that. It is easy to lose the plot as it were and of course if you are working on the creative side you need the stimulus of company. The book says as much, warning against isolation.

Having said that, being on your own is undoubtedly more conducive to getting it down.

* * *

Day 5 of Writing

And so it was the following morning.
    I was there again.
    Two mornings in a row.
    Apart from the day in the middle of course.
    Nine o'clock.
    At my table in the white room.
    Looking out the white-washed window at
    the white-washed wall of
    the house opposite.
    Ready to build on my opening line.

END OF MONTH REPORT

The month began with a flourish. Day 1, Mark read Danny's book from cover to cover. *Desafortunadamente*, Day 2, an urgent letter for the landlord interfered with progress. Day 3, Mark embarked on his opening line. Things were going nicely until the middle of the afternoon when he developed excruciating pain in his knee. Perhaps he was overdoing it, though he couldn't see the connection between his creative work and his physical injury. Day 4, he was under the knife. Through no fault of his own, barely another word was written in March despite the promising start. However, Mark assures me that he has been thinking, working things out in his head and, hopefully we can expect resumption of normal service in April.

5

APRIL

Easter is unpredictable. Unlike the first of January. Which falls on the first of January every year. My year, Easter fell first week of April. *Semana Santa* with it. All I knew of *Semana Santa* before coming to Spain was that a friend, whom I did not associate with religious fervour, had gone to Seville one year for Holy Week and had been beaten up. Strange on two counts:

1. Spain for Holy Week?
2. And why would you be beaten up? Outside a bar on the *Costa* in the early hours, sure. But Seville during religious ceremonies?

Long before the week itself, posters went up around the village. Even before that, I had been puzzled by posters from previous years in shop windows, like souvenirs. Bizarre, I thought, to advertise such a week, as you might a Beyoncé concert or a bullfight. The posters didn't actually say, "Come and enjoy" but that was the tenor of the anticipation rippling around the village. At home, we don't *look forward* to Holy Week. We get through it. Here, a spectacle was being prepared, a must-see.

In the run-up, the men of the *Ayuntamiento* nailed the Stations of the Cross into the walls of the village, first and last in the *plaza*.

* * *

Domingo de Ramos

Semana Santa began on a Sunday afternoon with the Blessing of the Branches. Olive branches. At home, Palm Sunday. We assembled at 5.30 at the statue of the tireless *Señora del Rosario* opposite my health centre. There was a good turnout. The men and women took the occasion seriously and dressed up. The children wore full-length cream robes, a bit like altar boys or adolescent Arabs. The priest was only a little late and got a warm reception. He changed into his vestments on the side of the road and began the short ceremony. It consisted of blessing the branches and distributing them among those present. Then we walked in spring sunshine down the hill past the supermarkets. The one on the left was closed because, as the owner explained to me, he is *"poco católico."* Others told me that he closes his shop at the drop of a hat. By reputation, the one on the right is open if there is a bob to be made and sure enough.

After Mass, the first procession of the week got under way. What had gone before, merely a warm-up. It was led by the men of the village bearing on their shoulders what they call a *trono* on which stood a massive statue of Jesus on a donkey – no light load – encouraged by the municipal band. Up and down the streets of the village, some so narrow that the swaying Jesus was brushing against the white-washed walls. All the time the bearers moving in step to the music. After an hour, Jesus and donkey had had enough – it was only the first day after all – and we returned to the church.

Semana Santa had begun.

* * *

Miercoles Santo

Spy Wednesday. Grandchildren not arriving until six. We only have three buses a day so I had to get the early one to be at the airport on time. I spent the day continuing my discovery of Malaga, this time knocking off the *Teatro Romano*. If there was anticipation in the village, it was small beer compared to the excitement in the city. Malaga was buzzing, reminding me of Easter Saturday at home, Lent over. But here we were only in the middle of the week. Much suffering still to come, celebration seemed previous.

The streets were lined with seating for the nightly processions that so far I had only seen on television. Each lamppost on *Calle Larios* had an arrangement of flowers, each building its coloured ribbon. As shops closed and families began to arrive for the procession, it was time for me to head to the airport.

Our granddaughters – identical twins of three years and their older sister of five – were coming for Easter with their parents. I was dying to see the little ones come through. When they did, pulling *Peppa Pig*, *Frozen* and Minnie Mouse behind them, one identical twin, I knew not which, broke rank and ran across the concourse into my arms. "Happy Easter Pops."

The procession was in full swing when we hit the city, moving in darkness and music around its centre.

"Jesus is coming at Easter with Easter eggs", declared first twin.

Up and down the main street. In and out of side streets.

"Where's He coming from?" asked Dad.

Restaurants heaving. Flowers for sale and roasted chestnuts.

"From Dead. Dead to Ireland", joined in second twin.

Massive statues borne shoulder-high on *tronos* by teams of bearers.

"From Dead?" Dad again.

Vía de Cruz.

"Yes. He has died. He's in Dead", second twin, explaining for second time.

We did our best to protect them from the more explicit depictions.

"He's not wearing any clothes", said first.

"He doesn't need them", replied second. "You don't wear clothes in Dead. Do you Daddy?"

"How would I know?" replied a getting-grumpy daddy. It had been a long day. "Ask Mummy."

They were spared reality crucifixions, at least. If not the spooky men in the hoods.

Older sister: "Daddy, I don't like this."

Dad: "I'm moving them to a secular school."

In the meantime, time for bed.

A A A

Viernes Santo

Good Friday. Early start. I had set my alarm. Unnecessary. Six-thirty, a dark man walking the dark village ringing a bell, summoning the men of the village to prayer. Only the men. *Vía de Cruz.* Due to begin at seven, I was assured that it wouldn't start before a quarter past so that when I turned up at half past, the procession had already left. In which direction? There were six. I discounted the flight of steps by the church. Down to five. We were doing the Stations of the Cross and I knew where the first and last were. I had seen them being erected in the *plaza*. But the twelve in between? No band to help me. No light. I could neither see nor hear the processors. If any had turned up. But they couldn't have gone far, I reasoned. It was a small place and they had to be slow-moving. Having said that, the *calles* are crooked and numerous. I caught them at the fifth.

I counted five and fifty men and one woman – my eighty-nine year old friend from the church. What was she doing here? I could see she was escorting a gentleman but that was hardly an explanation. Escorting a gentleman wouldn't get you into a gentleman's club in London. She seemed to be signalling to me that her companion wasn't the full Euro. This was making me anxious because he seemed perfectly alert to me. She kept pointing at him, tapping her temple furiously and sighing. She was doing all of this transparently, as the times demanded. I was in a foreign land and not familiar with the nuances of sign language as practised by the locals but felt sure that even in Spain a gentleman would not be pleased to see a friend signal him not all there. I was uneasy and moved up the procession.

It got light as we carried the Cross from station to station. Stopping at each for a reading and a prayer. Then on, singing. Not heavenly singing but we were doing our best. It was strange moving around the village in this way as it opened for business. Station to station along *Calle Estacion*, the main thoroughfare of the *pueblo*. Why so called? *Estacion* means station but there was no station here for bus or train. Just a view to the sea and, this Good Friday morning, sun surfing the rooftops of *Sayalonga*. On we went. Priest, mayor, former mayors and the men only of the *pueblo*. Following the Cross. Incense in the air and the smell of a joint from the fellow walking beside me.

At the twelfth station Jesus dies and so we stopped at the *cementerio* where this station had been placed and knelt on the pebbly road. I knelt on one knee only for fear of upsetting my *rodilla*. We waited longer there watching the sun inch up the mountain opposite.

Back to base, stations done. My friend, her care restored to his loved ones, invited me for a coffee. As we sat at the counter, locked into our sign language, I noticed the men around me having something stronger. *Anis*, I was told and joined them. It had been an early start after all and it was cold outside. I had no idea that *Señora* was going to pay. Walkers, oblivious to the ceremonies, were tying their laces in readiness for their assault on the *sierras*.

This was another of those ghastly penitential days. Two in the year. Only two. Thank God I'm not a Muslim. One down. And on this, the other, I was already drinking. Unlikely that Islam would be looking to me for a transfer. The only way to achieve damage limitation in the food and drink department, I decided, was to go for an early *siesta*. So, shortly after eleven, two coffees and a number of anis to the good, I took myself back to the bed and out of harm's way.

Looking around the village, I could find no evidence of a thirst for penance on the part of my neighbours. They throw themselves into their processions alright but they draw the line there. I'm not sure that fast and abstinence are in their DNA. Too full of *la vida* and living for that.

Of course there are exceptions to every generalisation. The gentleman processing blindfold was one. I was told later that if you commit a heinous sin then, traditionally, processing blindfold is a way back for the sinner. A heinous sin, mind you; no second-rate stuff. As if to compensate for this harshness, in Malaga, applying the Barabbas precedent, a prisoner is set free every Good Friday.

At three o'clock, I was startled from *siesta* by the bells of the church. Four chimes to mark an hour. Followed by three to mark this hour.

And then the bell-ringer was at large. It was Good Friday after all and he or she was free to ring the bells as loudly and for as long as he or she wished. Anyway I'd been asleep long enough.

Starting times in the mountains are aspirational and the procession due to start at ten that night didn't start until eleven. The hour was put to good use. The *plaza* filled, the band warmed up and Rodriguez, in black, and black glasses, was on hand to serve anyone who felt like it a little something to warm them up.

Eleven and the band moved up a gear. The lights of the village went out. We lit our candles. The lofty doors of the church clanked open. The *tronos* stepped out. Jesus on the Cross first, Jesus off the Cross second and *Nuestra Señora del Rosario*. Twelve shoulders to each: six front, six back.

Once in the *plaza*, a brief dance routine – bearers swaying to the music, forward, back, side to side – and the *tronos* were off. We were off too. Once more around the block. If I hadn't known the village before, I knew it then. Each *calle laberinto* of it.

The procession snaked its way.

Haunting music,

step,

sway.

Single beat of drummer boy.

Candles flickering.

Around this mountain village under black sky.

God help any restless soul stirring from sleep as the raised, not yet risen, Christ passes his bedroom window. At least we are spared the hooded gentlemen – who would scare the bejesus out of you – so prominent in the larger outings.

Journey over, the bearers halted outside the doors of the church for a final dance. High as the heavens themselves, the *tronos* dominated the packed *plaza*. The band played on. Jesus on the Cross, Jesus off the Cross and *Nuestra Señora* looking out over the dark *sierras*, all the time swaying from left to right, forwards and back, in time with the music. At last, the bearers turned under their loads and walked their *tronos* into the church to the applause of the pilgrims in the *plaza*.

* * *

DOMINGO DE RESURRECCION

Easter Sunday was wet. Our friends had warned us. Rain every Easter for six years. The final procession of *Semana Santa* was scheduled for midday. Twelve on the dot, doors opened, as did the heavens. As heavenly a downpour as I had witnessed. Villagers who had poured into the *plaza* and into their Resurrection finery for the procession were drenched and disappointed. An ecclesiastical decision was called for and the procession cancelled. We may have been lagging behind Malaga in the tables but no one complained. Back in the church, the band squeezed in and brought us through their Easter parade.

Jesus hadn't forgotten the eggs. He had carried them all the way from Dead and had given them to Rodriguez, in purple for Easter, to hide in the *plaza* for the egg hunt as soon as the rain stopped.

* * *

A week later, I was back in Sergio's. Champions League. Local team again. Family had returned to normal life in Dublin. I had returned to normal life here. It had been lovely having them, but no work done for the duration. You can't write a letter, let alone a novel, with little ones knocking on your door every ten minutes. "Pops, are you coming out to play?" Any more than you can write one in a cul-de-sac. No matter how hard I tried to explain, they couldn't understand. They were only three and five, for heaven's sake. What else is Pops for? And anyway the white room had been commandeered for their bedroom. Which of course made their grandmother complicit. I had been in favour of renting an apartment for them. Don't get me wrong. I love my family but, coming so close on the heels of the *rodilla*, they weren't helping productivity. And time was passing. Added to which, the weather had been awful. So, all in all I just had to go to Sergio's.

He didn't mention the book.

Malaga, blue and white, had qualified for the first time. Not only that but had made it through to the knock-outs. Fairy-tale stuff. Against Dortmund in the quarter-final. Second leg. Miraculously, they had two away goals in hand. 2–2 in Dortmund. No matter, no one gave them a chance, least of all the noisy Germans in the corner.

Leading 1–0 with eight minutes to go.

Bar on fire.

Except the noisy corner.

Drinks on the house.

Except the noisy corner.

Could the unthinkable happen?

Six minutes.

Against the run of play ... a goal ... Dortmund.

1–1.

No matter.

A draw would do.

The away goals.

Four minutes to go.

History already made. Bigger history beckoned.

Ninety minutes on the clock. 1–1.

Malaga through to the semi-finals.

Not yet.

Injury time. Three minutes.

How could there be three?

Two played.

One left.

Surely ...

GOAL ... Dortmund.

Tears.

The fire went out.

Except in the noisy corner.

* * *

It had been one of those matches, right up there, and a wonderful night. I had cheered with the locals and cried too. We had even congratulated the noisy corner. I had made new friends. Despite the rain, I was in high spirits walking home, determined to put the previous unfruitful week behind me. No visitors due for a while, I had a chance to get up a good head of steam. Momentum being of the essence.

Unfortunately, I had cheered and cried and drunk too much and slept through the alarm. Eleven when I woke. Always eleven. The high spirits had disappeared and an almighty headache filled the void. I decided that before going to the desk I would clear the backlog in the kitchen.

I was in the middle of the washing-up when the doorbell rang. Not something that happened very often. Previous time it had been two Jehovah Witnesses who didn't speak English. Apparently, there are a lot of them around. This time

"*Hola. Buenos días.*"

Charming young men from the gas company, almost as well-dressed as the Witnesses. Two in number. They greeted me in friendly unison when I opened the door. As I hadn't removed the rubber gloves, I was at a sartorial disadvantage.

"Never mind", they seemed to say as they marched past me into the kitchen.

Within seconds they were on their hands and knees dismantling the kitchen sink or, more precisely, the gas connection under it. Between them they hadn't a word of English. Not that it mattered. It was perfectly obvious what they were doing. What it had to do with reading the meter – which was why I had let them in the first place – I had no idea. They worked quickly within an ever-increasing circle of parts. As they dismantled, the tone of their chat became more grave. The word '*peligroso*' came into play.

Man number 1 looked at me
meaningfully.
He pointed to the gas cylinder.
When he had finished pointing,
he raised both arms towards the heavens and
shouted "boom" in an alarming voice.

Immediately, man number 2 also shouted "boom"
indicating a consensus.
Man number 1 pointed to last year's date
on a length of rubber, whereupon
both men jumped up
in a synchronised jump-up
as if there wasn't a moment to lose.
Man number 2, the writer,
filled out a bit of paper and
handed it to me to sign.

Up to that moment I hadn't thought about what was going on save
that they were interrupting my headache and delaying my return to
the desk. When he handed me a pen with which to sign the bit of
paper, on which I could see written three hundred and something Euro
I began to have reservations.

"*Telefono*", I said, picking up my mobile.

"*No necessario*", the writer said, tapping the bit of paper
impatiently.

I phoned Jill.

"Don't let them in", she said.

Good advice.

"Too late", I said.

"Will I send Reg up?"

"*No necesario*", I said, even in the crisis improving my Spanish.
"I'll handle it."

I put the phone down. Man number 1 shoved a '*contracto*' for five
years in front of me – the ante was being upped or the stakes raised,
whichever you prefer – and handed me a different pen. No shortage
of pens. I hadn't been a barrister for forty years without learning that
you don't sign something without first reading it. Unfortunately I had
already signed it without reading it. But not without muttering "provi-
sional" under my breath like any good golfer having lost a ball.

By then, the men, no longer charming, were looking for cash and
getting cross. All of a sudden, a seven-foot shadow fell across the
proceedings. Reg in the open doorway. What made Jill think that I
mightn't handle it? At first there wasn't enough room for all of his head.

He had to duck and dive. He could have been an All–Black lock, the size of him, except that he is English and going on seventy.

Shouting and pointing at the signed bit of paper, they stood their ground. Reg doesn't have any Spanish. He didn't need it.

"Out", he roared. One word. They took one look at him.

Standing their ground lost its charm. They grabbed what they could and ran.

"Thank you", I said to him. "I got us into a bit of a hole there."

"You sure did", and he laughed.

"Will they be back?"

"Not a chance", he said.

"I did sign one of the bits of paper." He handed me that week's *Costa News*:

"FAKE GAS INSPECTORS ARE BACK AGAIN"

"This scam is widespread in Andalucía and you should never allow such people into your home .... They especially target elderly people who live alone ...."

Reg was delighted with the 'elderly' bit. "They especially target elderly people who live alone", he kept repeating.

He suggested that I take up Spanish classes and then this sort of thing wouldn't happen. Rich from Reg. He'd been here twenty years and didn't have a word.

Mindful of the excess of the night before, I poured two large ones.

END OF MONTH REPORT

To be honest, April was never a runner. For one thing, Easter came early this year and for another Mark's entire family came out. How could he be expected to deliver in those circumstances? And he didn't disappoint. *Nada*, nothing. Not a word. I am beginning to lose confidence in Mark.

6

MAY

DAY 6 OF WRITING

Earmarked for writing at any rate. A chance look at the calendar told me that it was the first of May. Already? The book says it is important to take stock as I go along. Easy to fall behind without noticing. Accordingly, I gave the creative stuff a break, for the morning anyway. To carry out a Review. Something that is all the rage out there in the real world. Reviews. Companies going halfway around the globe to carry them out. So that they wouldn't be interrupted. I wouldn't be going that far.

I remember reaching a 440 yards semi-final at school. Long before Michael Johnson's time. And about a minute slower. I was inexperienced. Fixed my eyes on the favourite. Stuck with him. Came second. Good plan. In the final, I adopted the same tactic. With a variation.

I would overtake him in the surge for the line. Once more, my best friends – *the best laid schemes* – Shame that Burns fellow couldn't handle English. Emerging from the final bend, the favourite wasn't to be seen. A few other favourites had popped up in the meantime and they were all in front of me. It was a life lesson. Of course, like all life lessons, it never turned up again. Until now. Time therefore for my First Quarterly Review.

We had had a gruelling introduction to our new life. Well, I had had. According to the statistics – I had been keeping a diary – I had been on my own for seventy of the ninety days to date. In excess of 66% of the time. The statistics tell the story: *I* was bearing the brunt of the transition. I'm not saying that Helen wasn't doing her bit. She was earning the money after all and making the experiment possible. And, of course, it wasn't her fault that her boss wouldn't release her. But it wasn't exactly what being at the coalface was all about. I didn't say that to her of course.

Alone at the front, I was proud of my achievement. No mean feat I thought to myself unanimously over a bottle of Milhojo [€3.40 in Angeles's, €1.96 from the gasman]. Going on 64, as I had been back in March, and more or less alone, to pick up my roots and put them down if only for a year in a foreign land, one that only recently had embraced democracy.

Looking back, going forward, there were many positives to be taken from the quarter under review:

- Successful negotiations with the postal authority [Paco 2]
- Not being browbeaten by the elderly Spanish woman with her wares
- Commencing The Great Novel
- Well, getting the room ready
- In the air, the hint of an invitation from the book club to address them on Writing The Great Novel
- Undergoing surgery
- Self-injecting for nine days
- Taking on the Andalucían medical service and
- Taking no nonsense from them in the process

- Giving up the drink for [most of] Ash Wednesday

The list went on and on.

There can be no triumph without failure. I had to acknowledge that there had been negatives to be taken from the positives. One or two, no more – to be sorted in the second quarter:

1. The pancake had been a disappointment. I had to accept that.
2. I was missing Sky Sports. I had seen precious little of the Six Nations and had just missed the Master's. Wimbledon around the corner,
3. I had not made as much progress with Spanish as I had hoped for. I had joined a class alright. For beginners. Too advanced.
4. It couldn't be denied that I had started. The Great Novel was under construction. Unfortunately, in the course of this Review, it became clear that I had not made as much progress as I would have liked. Indeed, any progress at all. Compared to this negative, others paled into insignificance. This one went to the heart of matters. Could it be rectified in the second quarter?

The evidence:
Three pages.
Three months.
Five days in the white room out of ninety.
A work rate of five out of ninety or one page a month, depending on how you look at it.
There was no way in which this statistic could be presented in a favourable light.
According to the book, what is required is 2,000 words a day. 2,000. Even taking this at five days a week, that is 10,000 words a week, which is in excess of 120,000 words in three months.
I counted my three pages.
To be fair, packed pages. Single spacing. Every line filled:
605 words.
Oh dear.
What would Helen say?

Not of what great novels are made.

ETA would have to be revised.

Outwards: 20 years.

War and Peace didn't take that long.

God knows, there had been distractions.

How was I to know that I would lose a day to the charming gentlemen not from the gas company? Or three weeks to the *rodilla*. Or that *la* entire *familia* would turn up for the entire of *Semana Santa*. I'm not one for excuses but facts are facts: there had been distractions outside my control. It wasn't as if I had been up in Sergio's every night watching football and drinking pints. There wasn't football every night.

There is no role for fairness. Life is cruel like that. Second in the Olympics, no point in saying that you had your period or an ingrown toenail. It's a simple matter. Black and white. When the year is up, there is a completed novel or there is not. Twelve pages – current rate of progress – will not do the business.

I felt like I felt that night on the road to *Sayalonga*. Lost. In darkness. No one to help. How was I going to arrive at my destination? How was I even going to continue? Should I curl up in a corner of the *camino* and cry?

I was happy with my three pages. Knew them by heart. Well written, not a spare word. But writing a novel is like running a marathon. Being happy with how you run the first mile doesn't get you over the line.

Just as well I had undertaken this FQR, I reflected. Had I not, the under-productivity might have gone undetected. Surely, there was still time. Nine months. But radical measures were called for. My writing strategy would have to be revised. Back to the book. What had Guru to say? Nothing in the index under *rodilla* or *semana santa*. Nothing under *men not from the gas company*. But sure enough, a chapter on DISTRACTION. I wasn't the first.

Guru was on top of things. Aware of the problem and had no doubt about the solution. One word:

RUTHLESSNESS.

I couldn't believe it. It was as if I had gone to him on a one-to-one. He was talking to me. "Every writer, no matter how long in the tooth, is prone to distraction", he says. "It is a particular hazard for the rookie. Much easier to make a cup of coffee or do the shopping. Write a letter, send an email. Wonder how the kids are getting on. Anything but write, put words on the page. That has to change", he says. "Once you go into that white room" (he has a white room too), "you go in alone. You bring nothing with you." I knew exactly what he meant.

I made up my mind there and then to take steps. From then on, I would go into the white room alone, take nothing with me. Only ruthlessness.

"Helen, I can't come home for your birthday" was how I launched my campaign of ruthlessness later that day on the phone to my wife. "I'm sorry."

Pause.

Silence.

Oh dear.

"What do you mean you can't come home for my birthday?" she said slowly down the phone. It seemed self-explanatory. "You know how I feel about birthdays." I had been in Spain for three months. I couldn't be expected to remember every detail of our married life.

"Of course I do. And I want to come home for it. It's just that …".

"Just that what?" What is it about women and birthdays? It wasn't like I'd forgotten the day itself.

"It's the book. It's not exactly finished."

"But you've nine months to go?" What sort of understanding of the creative process was this?

"That's the point. Only nine months. Only three pages written."

"Three pages? What are you doing out there? Are you having an affair?" What sort of a question was that?

"There have been a lot of distractions. You know there have."

"Nonsense."

"My *rodilla*, for example."

"You're not still going on about your *rodilla*. Try having a baby", she said. Below the belt. Why does it always come back to that? We can't win that argument. We can't have a baby. Not yet anyway.

Maybe when we can, we'll find out that it's not all it's cracked up to be. For another day.

"If you got up earlier and drank less." Uncalled for.

"That's not fair." Since when did fairness come into it? Fairness didn't seem to matter anymore.

"It's just a weekend. Kids have arranged a surprise."

Another pause.

Another silence.

What made me think Helen would understand?

"Well?"

Ruthlessness?

I no longer had an option.

My campaign would have to be relaunched.

"Of course." Pause. Barely audibly, "I was only joking."

* * *

As far as I was concerned May was early summer. This was one thing that we had in common in the northern hemisphere: seasons. The locals did not agree. It didn't help that I kept confusing *verano* and *verduras*, summer and vegetables respectively. An easy confusion to make I think. So, for a long time, when I was arguing that summer begins in May, I was in fact saying that vegetables begin in May and when locals insisted that *verano* begins on the twenty-first of June I told them that on the twenty-first of June we are halfway through vegetables. On the other hand, in the restaurant, wanting vegetables, I ordered summer.

Anyway, during whichever season it had been since my arrival in February, a mixture of spring and vegetables, as I thought, or spring alone as they thought, the weather had been awful. That much they agreed.

We had had more than our share of rain and cold. More than enough of Moorish mist wrapping itself around the mountain like a burqa. A long period when Maroma couldn't be seen. It was unlikely that the weather was worse in Westport. At least there we would have had the right clothes and no language barrier. Certainly, this wasn't the climate that had enticed me to Andalucía. 333 days of sunshine how are you?

The locals kept telling us to wait for July and August, when the heat would be unbearable. I kept telling them that if I didn't get a taste soon I would be unbearable. The municipal *piscina* at the bottom of the village across the road from *San Anton's ermita* had not been inviting to that point. However, even if I had wanted to swim, I couldn't because there was no water in it and there wouldn't be any until June; the spring or vegetables end of June I was too cross to clarify.

We have a wonderful roof terrace that you could land a helicopter on. So far that hasn't been necessary. In the event of a fire on the mountain, the *Ayuntamiento* is permitted by law to take water from private swimming pools. In the event of such a fire, the *Ayuntamiento* can land on our roof, though why they would do that I have no idea as we don't have a swimming pool. We don't even have a garden.

From what I can see, the men who come here do so because they've run out of planning permission at home. Their joy is to build and, if not building, to be in their sheds making things. Eventually, when the house at home can't take another extension and the shed is chock-a-block with things they've made, they come to Spain and start again. They find a shack, as tumbledown and inaccessible as possible. Preferably, one that requires knocking down and rebuilding from scratch. All the better if it has neither electricity nor water and the nearest shop is a time zone away. The missus has little say in the matter while Don Juan, the vendor, who has moved on to better things, pays the new arrivals to take it off his hands.

I will arise and go now
and go to the South of Spain
and a small casita build there
    ...
Sorry W.B.

No thanks. The *pueblo*. Shop around the corner. Air conditioning. Ship-shape. Not a Black & Decker on site. Lemons are for gin and tonic Mr Stewart, not for driving over.[*] Ok, so no Sky Sports. It's a deal. You can't have everything.

* * *

To each village its character.
  To each its characters.
  Angeles, my first *amiga* in *Canillas*, is a red-headed workaholic.
  She runs her shop single-handed. Early morning till late night. A home and a husband to boot. At all hours she is to be heard slopping buckets of water over her flowers and her front patio.
  Her shop is not busy if by busy you mean full of customers, but there is a stream of callers. Usually, when I call, there is no one there, not even herself, and I have to wait a while before she comes on the scene. Oftentimes I have to let a roar out of me. Eventually she shows. Aproned, out of breath and explaining. She was busy preparing the next *comida*, which she describes, blowing little kisses with her fingers to indicate how *estupenda*. The closing time for the afternoon depends on progress in the kitchen. Sometimes I feel I am intruding, that I should leave her get on with her cooking and sneak back out, as unnoticed as when I entered. On one occasion, I was doing just that when she arrived. I felt as if I had been caught red-handed with a string of *chorizo* up my T-shirt and started apologising profusely.
  If there is no one there when I go in, the shop is in darkness. It is a dark and deep shop and needs lighting even during the day. But it doesn't get it until Angeles arrives. Whether this is an economy on her part or a device to keep the temperature down I don't know. The business end of the shop, by which I mean where you pay, is well down the shop so to get there you are taking your life in your hands. Likewise, if you are trawling the shelves while waiting for herself. God help you if someone has dropped a yogurt and the contents are meandering down the aisle like a local *arroyo*. Or, if someone has forgotten to cover the hole to the basement. An accident waiting to happen. What does Spanish law say about Occupiers' Liability and

---

[*] *Driving over Lemons* by Chris Stewart.

Dangerous Premises, I wondered. Ever the barrister. Whatever it says, it wasn't bothering Angeles.

When there is someone there, the fact that anyone else is queuing up behind that person in no way expedites the transaction or cuts short the conversation that goes with it. I am not in any hurry so it doesn't matter a damn. But for all we know, the customer behind has an urgent letter to post and Paco 2's half-hour may be nearly up. Angeles has put the items in a plastic bag, written the price of each in pencil in her copybook, totted, handed the items over and has her elbows on the counter in a state of listening. The customer has parted with the money and taken delivery of the shopping. Time to move on. Adiós. Goodbye. Particularly if there is a queue forming. No. The incumbent has Angeles's exclusive attention until the conversation comes to its natural conclusion. It matters not how many people are waiting. If the conversation goes on for such a long time that it might interfere with the *comida*, then Angeles may start making yapping signals with her fingers when the customer she's talking to isn't looking. She is a democrat however and, when my turn comes, I will receive the same attention, down to the yapping fingers if called for no doubt.

Angeles has no English – an observation, not a criticism. I have no Spanish – an observation and a criticism. Nonetheless, somehow, we converse and get on. At least I think so. We range far and wide. *Qué calor*, in summer. *Qué frío*, in winter. How there is always so much *lluvia*, rain, in England – no matter how often I tell her it's Ireland. Somehow we manage a laugh, especially when I tell her "my woman", *mi mujer*, is back in, I give up, England. With a big smile on her face and rubbing her hands together in conspiratorial fashion, she pops a handful of chocolate goodies into the plastic bag, the price of which doesn't make it into her copybook. She puts her finger to her lips. I do the same. *Hasta luego*, till the next time, as she turns off the light.

END OF MONTH REPORT

To be honest, at the end of April, I was beginning to have my doubts about Mark and his novel. I didn't doubt his sincerity and his ambition. He wants to write this book. I can see that. And there have been obstacles. Not all of his making. I just felt that there might be something missing in the determination department, that place where, come what may, you are programmed to deliver. I was pleased then when he told me about his First Quarterly Review. That showed maturity I thought. And I admired how he faced up to the lack of progress and sought a solution. June is crucial. It's now or never.

7

JUNE

We had a lovely week at home for Helen's birthday. I had had reservations initially. In the end I felt I had made the right decision. There wasn't any other. Ok, so it wasn't a significant birthday – 60 next year – but birthdays are birthdays and they mean more to women.

Ruthlessness tempered by wisdom, the wisdom of knowing when you can't win. And, as Helen had shrewdly said, sure there was still plenty of time.

There was also an unforeseen advantage. For my project. It had been good for me to get out of the village. I had got a bit stale. To get home, recharge my batteries, put a bit of light between me and what I was trying to do. Having carried out my Review I was then able to reflect on it and make a few decisions about where I was going.

One thing in particular, as I was reflecting: my plot. I had to accept that my output hadn't been great and I had my explanation for that. But I began to think that possibly it was my plot. It wasn't exciting me. Was my plot holding me back, I wondered. Should I be thinking about an alternative plot? These were demanding questions and had only just come to light.

Undoubtedly, I was having a doubt. What the Spanish call a *duda*. Indeed the more I thought about it, the more *duda* I was having. The Spanish say *agitarse en las dudas*, which loosely translated means arsing around in the *dudas*. Which is exactly what I was beginning to do.

There was only one thing for it. Notwithstanding the birthday celebrations, I had to have a word with Helen.

She put it succinctly. "The question is", she said, "is this a self-doubt that has value and should be entertained, or is it a self-doubt which should be banished instantly." In a nutshell. I congratulated Helen on her identification of the issue. However, it didn't get me any nearer to an answer.

"It could be either", I said hopelessly.

She pushed on.

"Have you an alternative plot?" Now, that I felt was a superior question because the fact was that I thought I felt an alternative plot stirring within me. Like a child in the womb, though I had no idea how that felt, as Helen had been quick to point out.

"It isn't as if you had written a hundred pages", she added. Helen had a habit of labouring her better points.

"What about this? A fellow goes off to do exactly what I'm doing, only maybe he's younger and unattached."

"He's not going to restore a house in the country and rear hens, is he?"

"God forbid."

As far as we got. Birthday beckoned.

Before I knew it, my time was up and I was back in the white room. Still thinking.

* * *

Plot.

Plot.

Plot.

Decisions. Decisions. Decisions. I never had any difficulty making up my mind when I was in practice. How to run a case. Which witnesses to call. What questions to ask. Whether or not to settle. Plead guilty or not guilty. High stakes. Client could be in jail tomorrow.

Not here. Here I was indecisive. My experience as a barrister of no assistance.

Ruthlessness had failed. That much I knew. Fell at the first hurdle. Helen's Brook. Not surprising really. Formidable opposition, Helen and her birthday.

How to come back? Mrs Thomas was right. *Do not go gentle into that good night.* Lock him in the shed until six and don't let him out until he's written six poems, one for every hour.

Ruthlessness would just have to get back up on its legs and ride again. June would be the turning point, the make-or-break month. Starting with rising. I would buy an expensive alarm clock and set it for five to nine and then when the nine o'clock bells rang I would jump out of bed and be at my desk at ten. Get the day off to a good start. Early bird and all that. I appreciate there are writers who get up at six every morning but that's their business. Horses for courses. Maybe they go for a boozy lunch.

So, what about the plot? Carry on? Start again? Was the fellow in *Jerez* right after all? I was on a year out. Maybe it wasn't a good idea to be fixated on the forty or so when I was in.

It worked. June the first. A Monday. First day of the week. The alarm went off, the bells rang and I was at my desk at ten. The white walls looked on as the words poured onto the page. No question of writer's block. I couldn't have stopped them even if I had wanted to. I was astonished. So were the walls. I hadn't experienced this previously in my writing career. I felt possessed. I couldn't get one sentence down before the next came rushing into my head. I needed a secretary to take the sentence that was coming second.

I had read about this. Artists going into a field and painting in the searing sun for hours on end. Writers writing through the night. No care for rest or nourishment. The only thing on their minds to get it down. This was how I felt. The words fell on the page in shape and the story told itself.

Hours passed. Pages filled. Not even a coffee break. The workers in the fields broke for the Angelus. Not me. Eventually, at six o'clock, I collapsed, exhausted. I couldn't write another word. I couldn't hold the pen. Eight hours on the trot. I had done this often of course as a barrister reading briefs. This was different.

There was only one thing for it. I took myself off to Sergio's terrace and ordered a pint. I sat there for an hour or more staring at the sun and the sky and the planes passing overhead. In a trance. I couldn't speak. I was overjoyed. This was what it was like to be a writer.

The next day, the same. Too good to be true. Five to nine; nine; desk at ten. The Guru said that you should always begin the next day with what you had written the day before. So far, there hadn't been a next day so this was a novel experience. I was nervous. Maybe what I had written the day before was gibberish. I read it. All ten pages, two thousand words of it. Two thousand words. I had hit the target. And it wasn't gibberish. Not perfect. Not bad. Something to build on.

The doorbell rang. I didn't hear it. It rang a second time. It could only be Lourdes, my wonderful neighbour. Her *modus operandi* – though she wouldn't have recognised it as such –was to ring the bell twice in quick succession and, if not answered immediately, to go for the door handle. As I came down the stairs, she was crossing the sitting room purposefully, as was her wont. She placed a paper bag with something in it on the table and sat down.

I thanked her for her present of the night before. When I had got back from Sergio's there was a plastic bag hanging from the door handle. As happened from time to time. I suppose presents have been delivered like this for centuries. Soap. The sort of soap you get in one of those fancy body shops. Rough stuff. Holes in it like emmental. Looks like lard or one of my pancakes. The neighbours were great for leaving in presents: avocados, oranges and the like. If I wasn't there, they would put them on the door handle without their name so that I would have to make discreet enquiries the next day as to who my benefactor was.

Lourdes made it clear. Last night's bag was not from her. It was from Fatima. She knew by the smell of it. Both women became wonderful friends and neighbours to us but never to one another. They couldn't stand one another. To date I had been unsuccessful in my attempts to get to the bottom of this.

She opened her bag and placed a year's supply of lard on the table. I thanked her profusely. She took each block up in her hand and sniffed it and passed it to me to sniff. She kept repeating "*precioso*." Soap is *masculino*. Then she emptied Fatima's bag and uttered what I'm sure was the word inferior. She kept running her thumb and forefinger across her mouth in that zipping fashion that denotes not a word. Specifically, not a word to Fatima. I thanked her again and again and I started that zipping thing to indicate that she could count on me in her conspiracy.

A few evenings before this, I had been on my roof terrace appreciating the beautiful evening. In particular, studying the sun setting on the *Rif* mountains opposite. The sound of the birds and the scent of the flowers. All of a sudden, an "*hola*." Not another wine-seller? Lourdes. Eighty-five years of age. On her roof. A proper roof. A sloping, tiled roof. Wouldn't take a helicopter. Ten at night. Painting or grouting or something. I hadn't spotted her. How could I? Her hair is the same colour as the roof tiles. I noticed after she retired for the night that she had left her cloths attached to the television aerial in case she forgot to bring them up with her the following night.

I didn't like being disturbed once I got started. It was hard enough to get started. Sometimes these visits took a while so that when my visitor left I was at my wits' end and had to go off for refreshment to recover my equilibrium. More time lost. Not today. Lourdes was gone, perhaps sensing my intent, and I was back at my desk in full flood.

I knew what it was.

All those times when I had been off the pitch and unable to do my writing had not been wasted.

There may have been nothing on the page to show for it and maybe the novel didn't progress but that didn't mean nothing was happening. Under the radar, little legs were paddling furiously, story developing, sentences – telling sentences – forming, so that when the time came, it all spilt out in a torrent of creativity and filled the page.

Meet my new hero, Benedict. Ben for short. A war correspondent with the *Irish Times*. Short stories published in the *New Yorker*. Not bad for a fellow in his mid-thirties. Everything was going swimmingly until, out of the blue, the tide turned and so did his wife. Veronica, his beautiful wife of only a few years, came home one evening – he was watching the Tour de France on the television at the time – and announced that she was lesbian.

"I'm lesbian", she said. Just like that. Needless to say, this came as a bit of a shock to Ben.

"I'm shocked", he said. The cyclists continued cycling through the French countryside.

There had been nothing in their sexual relationship to suggest that she was being short-changed in any way. As it were. Quite the contrary. She was mad for the bed and indeed it didn't always have to be the bed. Tables, cupboards, you name it. They'd been there. Maybe it wasn't all about the bed. What else could it be?

"Pity she didn't discover it a bit earlier", his best man said to him on a different day.

"How would that have helped?" Ben wanted to know.

He was very much a modern man. Travelled to work by skate-board. Something like lesbianism wasn't going to faze him. Unless of course it turned out that his wife had it. He wasn't that modern.

She was a high-flyer. Her career brought her all over the world. She spent more time in airports than at home with Ben. Not her fault. The travel went with the job. Anyway, that wouldn't explain her conversion to lesbianism. Conversion to a pilot maybe. He could have handled that.

He was at a loss. What to do? He pleaded with her.

"You're not a lesbian", he said repeatedly. To no avail.

"It's a *fait accompli*", she said. His best man was going on holidays.

They split up quickly. There didn't seem to be any point in doing it differently. He was distraught. He took to the drink. What else could he take to? After six months of solid drinking, he stopped. He would take a leave of absence for one year from the newspaper and he would go to Spain and write a novel. Everyone was doing it. And anyway, it was something that had been on his agenda for a date in the future.

Indeed, it had been on their agendas. He was getting maudlin. Why not now? He settled his golden retriever in a good home and off he went.

And so it continued. Week on week. Word by word.

At end of June, I counted. Thousands upon thousands of words. I couldn't believe it. Where on earth had they all come from?

25,002 words to be exact. It had taken me an hour to count them. I was nearly there. In a single month. The Guru said that 60,000 would do it and certainly 70,000. Another month and then a bit of fine-tuning. The Christmas market was back on the table.

I rang Helen in the excitement.

"That's fantastic", she said.

What else could she say? Still, it was good of her to say it. She sounded in good form. She was going out with her sisters for dinner, she told me. All six of them. They hadn't been out together for a while. Probably a month. They were celebrating their birthdays. All born in June. Different Junes. Imagine. Except Helen who nearly was.

"I told you you had plenty of time." Harking back. Her birthday in May. Sometimes she just couldn't let go. "By the way, I nearly forgot. Met a fellow at a party the other night. A publisher. I told him you were writing a book. He said to send it in."

How could you nearly have forgotten to tell me that?

"What a coincidence. I've just got to 25,000 and a publisher is showing interest."

"When you say showing interest ... he suggested you send it in."

"I know, I know, but it's something. Love to your *hermanas*." My Spanish coming on.

* * *

"You look *muy contento*", said Sergio as soon as I hit the counter. I hadn't seen him in June apart from that first night.

"I am", I replied, "*muchísimo contento. Escribiendo.* Book. *Libro*" and I made a writing gesture with my right hand. "25,000 words."

"*Qué?*" I was stretching things. I took my pint back out onto the terrace to thank the sun and the sky and the passing planes. I wanted to thank the poet from *Jerez* as well but I had no way of contacting him. I couldn't even remember his name. After all, it was he who said to ignore the law. Mumbo-jumbo he had called it. And his mother a leading lawyer in London. Write about what you don't know, he had said. I didn't know about lesbians. Maybe if I put 'Poet from *Patagonia*' in the search engine, something might come up. He said he was published. I could buy his poetry online as a thank you.

Sergio followed me with a plate of olives. He knew I was happy and he knew why but not precisely why. He slapped me on the shoulder. We were mates.

For the first time in a month, I slept through the alarm. For the first time in a month, I had treated myself. After a month off it, something that did not come easily to me, I had had a little more to drink than was absolutely necessary. After all, there was the launch to plan.

Someone told me that when Beckett finished *Waiting for Godot* he took himself off to Brittany, or was it Normandy, exhausted, to recover. Of course, he was writing in French. I don't know what the connection between Brittany, or is it Normandy, and exhaustion is. But anyway that is what he did and where he went. I had no intention of travelling. I was writing in English. But, for sure, I was taking off the first weekend of July. For *Feria*. I had earned it.

END OF MONTH REPORT

Ten out of ten, Mark.
Mirabile dictu.
El breakthrough.
Keep your eye on the ball now.
You've earned your *Feria*.

9

JULY

July and August are set aside for *Feria*. You could argue that the entire year is set aside. Every village has an annual *Feria*. Once a month. But *Feria* in July or August is the mother of all *Ferias* or, as we used to say before Saddam Hussein came along, the daddy of them all.

Each village has one. And each neighbouring village. So between one *Feria* and another, July and August are not good months for getting things done.

I can well understand why in northern territories we need Christmas to cheer up the darkness of December. Think about it. What would it be like having to get from October to March without Christmas? Indeed, having thought about it, Iceland and places would be entitled to a few Christmases every winter. But Spain in summer is in no need of cheering up and of course if you enjoy a drink it is harder to handle the

81

day after in these months when the sun shines relentlessly. There hadn't been one drop of rain in June and hardly a cloud. We had been told that we would find July and August unbearable and we were about to find out.

I decided to test the appetite for *Feria*. I bumped into San Pablo, who had looked after me so well when I was hospitalised back in February. He was sitting on a bench at the top of the road down to *Archez*. Where you'd often find him.

"Are you looking forward to *Feria*?" I asked him, sort of. In Spanish, sort of. All he would have received from me would have been a gesticulation and the word '*Feria*' with a raised intonation and possibly a raised shoulder to indicate a question mark. It was up to him to make what he could of it after that.

Pablo, with whom I normally have a pleasant, cheerful conversation, got very cross. I was taken aback. It seemed like a harmless question, not one that would get either of us into trouble. He started jumping around the place and putting his hands over his ears and then his head and emitting noises. I realised immediately that I had pressed a wrong button. It was necessary to change the topic of conversation.

"*Todo bien?*" "All well?" I went for, cheerily.

Another wrong button. It was if I had told him his horse had fallen at the first. There wasn't much room left in Pablo's cross department but what was left he took over immediately. I moved on and left him to whatever was tormenting him. Which seemed to be me mainly.

Pablo apart, the village is proud of its *Feria* and was looking forward to this one, the real one, on the first weekend of July, as the high point of the season. Very helpfully, a booklet of advertisements containing the programme of events for the three days, in Spanish and a variation of English, was available free of charge from the *Ayuntamiento*.

DAY 1 OF FERIA

At nine in the morning on Friday the first of July, the municipal band toured the village announcing the commencement of *Feria*. This was entirely unnecessary as everyone in the village already knew. They had talked of little else since *Semana Santa* and there were posters everywhere. Unfortunately, due to the early start, I missed it.

The band was back at eleven with an expanded portfolio, by which time I was up and dusted. Not only playing lovely music but collecting ribbons. These ribbons had been prepared by *las muchachas del pueblo*, the girls of the village, in the days before. The band played outside Angeles's *supermercado* where two gorgeous *muchachas* were waiting with their ribbons to hand them over. And then on to the next house and the next *muchachas* and so on until the village had run out of ribbons.

After an eventful morning, there was a time-out until the evening.

At 7.30 we assembled. The *Corrida de Cintas a Caballo*. *Corrida de toros* is a bullfight but *corrida* without the *toros*? The gist of it would seem to be "the running of the ribbons on horseback."

Mercifully, it was a shaded stretch of roadway above *Plaza 2* where the evening events of *Feria* would take place. A rope had been attached to lampposts on either side of the street at a height of about ten feet. The coloured and embroidered ribbons, which had been collected from the *muchachas* during the morning, each by its own hook hanging from the rope, fluttered in the welcome breeze. Fifteen riders, each carrying a finely pointed pencil, assembled at the starting line. In theory one ribbon for each rider. One by one they rode their horses at gathering pace towards the rope of ribbons, one hand guiding the horse, the other guiding the pencil. The aim, to score a hook. The successful rider rode on triumphantly. Ribbon flowing in the wind. The unsuccessful rider simply rode on. To the holder of the most ribbons, the prize.

Not easy. Horsemanship and courage required in stiff measure and eye-to-hook coordination, and that's just for the rider. For the horse, band and bangers have to be blocked out and the revving of the motor bikes whose riders, impatiently, await their turn to emulate the *caballeros*.

I couldn't believe the speed at which the horses, roared on by the crowd, galloped up the street. Their riders – "look, no hands" – standing in their stirrups lining their pencils up to their targets. Some of the riders had success, some more than once, others came away ribbonless but not downhearted, for the villagers gave their support in equal measure as each rider made his raid.

I had discovered during *Semana Santa* that when a programme says that something is to begin at a particular time, it's in the nature of a helpful guide rather than an imperative. It doesn't follow that it will start at that time or indeed at any time close to that time. Punctuality is for buses and trains. And the English.

The next instalment was programmed to start at 22.30. I descended to *Plaza 2*. I don't know what happened to the rest of the crowd but they didn't come with me. Perhaps they went home for a *siesta* or something to eat. I was on my own. Pop-up bars were popping up, bouncing castles were bouncing up, the band for the evening warming up. A single dodgem cruising round and round like a headless chicken.

It was unusual for me to be on time. For the Spanish too apparently. When there was still no one there an hour later, I began to think that the band had got it wrong in the morning when they announced the commencement of *Feria*. Perhaps they were early by a day, or possibly a week. Perhaps they were just practising. It didn't bother me. It was a delightful Mediterranean evening and I was enjoying the *vino* and *tapas* as I listened to the band going through its paces.

According to the programme, the last event of the evening, "*Bailamos con la orquesta hasta qué el cuerpo aguante.*" Meaning, I speculated, "we'll dance with the band till we drop." Not starting till 2.30 a.m. Helpful guide, remember, not an imperative. By my calculation, more likely to be 4.30 a.m. As it was only the first night of *Feria*, I decided to keep my powder dry and around one o'clock, as the Spanish were beginning to arrive in numbers, I made my way home.

As I walked through *Plaza 1*, I noticed that the door of the church was open. Strange, I thought. It isn't open during the day. I looked in. Dark. Couldn't see anything. I heard voices. Two voices of the village, women I knew well, one ironing, the other keeping her company. I greeted them and went on my way, leaving them to their chat and their ecclesiastical domestics.

My Swedish friend, affectionately nicknamed Jantonica, told me the following morning that the music had gone on until 7. She knew. Her house hangs over *Plaza 2* and she didn't sleep a wink. Around five, she considered invading the pitch in her nightie and requesting a ceasefire.

Day 2 of Feria

At ten on Saturday morning, a concession to the lateness of the night before, the band was back. This time, according to the programme, *anunciando el segundo día de Feria*. Once again, a complete waste of time. Once again I missed it.

Second day of *Feria* was for the children. Mainly. At midday we assembled in *Plaza 1* for their events, after which there was a presentation. Presents were thrown from Dulcinea's balcony. One came in my direction. In error. I was too old by sixty years. By instinct I put out my hand. I had done the same at a pantomime in London in the fifties. 'If I Had a Hammer' by Trini Lopez was all the rage at the time. Norman Wisdom was throwing rubber hammers into the audience and I caught one. Still have it.

On another occasion, I won Kim Novak's nightie in a raffle in the Gaiety Theatre in Dublin. But that's another matter. This time it was neither a hammer nor a nightie and I didn't keep it. It was a soft doll and I gave it to a little one near me. She was thrilled. She kept looking at the soft doll. Then at me. Then back at the doll. As if trying to understand the sequence of events that led to the doll landing in her lap.

It was time for lunch. *Paella* for everyone, courtesy of the *Ayuntamiento*.

By the time the music started, it was scorching in the *plaza*. Even the dogs had sloped off. Mid-afternoon. Mid-summer. Mid-thirties, at least. Not a hint of a forgiving breeze. A cover that had been put up over the *plaza* provided essential shade but no respite from the intoxicating heat. It was no time to be out and about. The DJ had chosen well. An electrifying beat. A machine that looked like it might spit out tennis balls spat out foam instead. Snowballs of foam. At last, *La Fiesta de la Espuma!*, The Foam Party. I had heard of it. Within minutes the *plaza* was transformed. Yesterday's restaurant a bubble-bath of foam.

La Plaza rocked.

La Plaza scorched.

La Plaza filled with foam.

At first, toddlers.

Then adults.

Normal, normally sane, adults walked into it in their clothes without a thought, clapping their hands and dancing and singing. Normal, normally sane, adults. They didn't have a chance.

The pounding heat

beat

the searing sun.

There was only one thing to do,

let go.

So you did and you joined in and you danced your heart out in the blazing sun of a July afternoon in the Andalucían mountains.

Thank God for the fellow with the hose. He could have made a fortune. Even the four middle-aged ladies who arrived from London in their frocks were grateful for his attention.

Eventually, we too sloped off.

Like the dogs.

"Saturday night and I just got paid." The big one. All roads led to our village. I ignored the timetable and arrived at midnight. Still too early. The early ones came an hour later. Eventually, *Plaza 2* was full and heaving. At one end, children soaring on castles and trampolines. In the middle, their elders soaring on alcohol and chatting in the corrals provided. You could even have hot chocolate and *churros* – rings of deep-fried batter for dipping in the chocolate – if you were so minded. At the far end, bands alternated between two stages and dancers of all ages were in full swing. Led by a fellow of my age in running gear, dancing with everyone and no one, stomping out the steps without rest for as long as I was there. A man possessed. Joyfully possessed by the music and the rhythm. He bore no resemblance to the man striding purposefully through the village in the morning on his way to his desk in the *Ayuntamiento*.

About four, I had given it as much as I had to give and made a move. I was on my own. No one else stirring. Neither the mothers nor their little ones asleep in their arms. The church door was firmly closed. As I went in my door, I could still hear the music. But that was the last of it as far as I was concerned. I was asleep before I hit the pillow.

DAY 3 OF FERIA

After back-to-back nights of *feria*-ing, the organisers gave us the day off. The finale began with Mass at 7.30 in *Plaza 1*. Mass got in everywhere. The priest was half an hour late. The choir sang. The sun shone. It was still hot. The women and children dressed in stunning traditional costume. *Nuestra Señora del Rosario*, Patron of the Parish, in a magnificent pink dress under a magnificent royal blue cloak, stole the show. She had left her niche above the altar and, back on her *trono*, was filling the doorway of the church, raring to go. Those on holiday looked on in bewilderment from their restaurant windows and hotel balconies. Only the previous day, *Plaza 1* had been full of foam.

Party time for *Nuestra Señora*. Thirty-four bearers in royal blue cloaks descended upon her. The very cloaks that the ladies had been ironing in the church two nights earlier. The bearers lifted her and her twenty-foot-long *trono* onto their burly shoulders. Mighty men. The municipal band, without which nothing in *Feria* moved, led the way. Behind the band, Herself, her bearers, bodies aching from the load, and the people of the village. Once again, up and down the narrow streets. *Nuestra Señora's* turn to bounce off the white walls. Eventually arriving at *Plaza 2* for the firework display. When that was over, she was carried to the fire station, where she took her place alongside the fire engine. From there, her candles flickering, she kept an eye on *Feria's* final offering.

We were a mixed bag of a party. Ex-pats and locals. Lourdes and Fatima at separate ends. Jill and Reg. Angeles of the *supermercado*. A reluctant Pablo. In the distance, the dour doctor. The mayor and his wife. Jantonica joined us with news that her Korean friend had been thrown out by his partner and was now sleeping in a tent in her garden. As if that wasn't enough, his dog had bitten a former mayor, who was sitting with his family at the next table, and has to be put down.

The party went on and on. We drank and we danced under a clear sky and we improved our Spanish. I threw in the towel about two. I was running out of towels. Over the nights of *Feria*, I had an attendance rate of 32 per cent. Not good enough. The Spaniards don't do the percentage game. I met Abuela and Abuelo, Granny and Grandad, my neighbours, no spring chickens, the next day. They had been there each evening till the bitter end. 7 a.m., 6 and 6 respectfully. And weren't impressed by my early departures. I wasn't at the races.

*   *   *

Feria over, it was back to the drawing board. Could the pace be sustained? Had it been a flash in the pan? I was about to find out. The next 25,000 beckoned.

I decided to *festina lente* and not bother with Monday. I was in no fit state. I had read that Hemingway liked to write on a hangover but I wasn't Hemingway and I didn't like bullfights. I declared Monday a *dies non*.

I had to bear in mind that Helen was due back later in the month, followed by the grandchildren for August. June had been an extraordinary month and if I could repeat it I would be in pole position for when my guests arrived.

*   *   *

Tuesday morning. My alarm went off, the bells struck and I was in the white room for ten o'clock. Ready to resume where I had left off the other side of *Feria*. At eleven the doorbell rang. The handle wasn't touched so it wasn't Lourdes. Instead, Paco 2 with a registered letter. Registered no less. Spanish stamp. Paco excited. Who in Spain would be sending me a letter, he wanted to know, let alone a registered one?

I sat down. Paco read it over my shoulder.

"Dear Mark,

Unfortunately, we have not met but your reputation goes before you and I look forward to rectifying that omission very soon.

I am the President of the *Federico García Lorca* Book Club of *Canillas* and *Cómpeta*. But not for much longer as my year is coming to a close. We are the oldest book club in Andalucía.

The members have asked me to invite you to speak at our last meeting of the year on the topic of *Writing a Novel*. Traditionally, our last meeting is the highlight of the year when we invite a celebrity writer to address us. I apologise for the short notice but we have been let down at the last minute by well-known novelist and your colleague Sebastian Donaldson, who has been required by his publisher to go on a book tour of the US to promote his latest bestseller, *A Mosquito on the Wall*.

I also apologise for the fact that I am not familiar with your work but will put that right between now and the 21st July. Perhaps you would be good enough to confirm that I will find you on Amazon.

Thanking you in anticipation,

Dolores Kensington."

"I didn't know you were a writer", Paco 2 said when I finished. I didn't know he had a word of English.

Madre mía. What a well-crafted and generous invitation. When Helen had said about speaking to the book club that first week, I hadn't taken it seriously. I had assumed it was in the nature of a politeness on the part of the member of the book club to whom she was speaking. But now here I was six months later receiving the formal invitation. From the oldest book club in Andalucía, no less. Alright so they had been let down, but I didn't mind playing second fiddle to the great Sebastian Donaldson. I wasn't proud like that. Particularly when I hadn't written anything.

"I'm very flattered", I said to Helen on the phone.

"And so you should be", replied Helen. "They're a sophisticated bunch by all accounts."

"But I can't possibly accept."

"And why not?"

"For the same reason I gave you the first time you mentioned it. I haven't written anything. I'd feel a fraud."

"Nonsense", said Helen. "Haven't you been a barrister for forty years?"

My wife didn't have a high opinion of my profession.

"What happens when they ask me what I've written?"

"Tell them. Nothing. But you're putting it right. You've just completed 25,000 words. It may be 40 by then. Your publisher is very pleased."

"But ...".

"No buts. You're on your way. They're lucky to have you, a soon-to-be bestselling novelist." She was very persuasive. "I'll be back for it. I get in on the 20th." There was no way out.

Dolores may not have known me. I knew her. A formidable woman. One of those ice-cool maiden types you'd be terrified to ask to dance. I had looked on from a distance when I had seen her in *Cómpeta*. A former Miss Northern Norway who fancied herself and her intellect and had married into a wealthy English family.

I decided to go for it. I accepted her kind invitation, suggested we meet to see what precisely she had in mind and gave her my email address. She replied immediately. Nothing wrong with her efficiency department. She didn't think a meeting would be necessary. Anyway she was very busy for July what with the end of her presidency and a number of summer engagements. I had the title of the talk and really she didn't think she could be of much assistance to an experienced writer. Presumably I had done this many times before.

Not exactly what you would call a charm offensive. However, consistent with the impression I had formed. Her personal assistant must have written the invitation.

I was on my own. No Dolores. Effectively no Helen, except on the phone. Three weeks to come up with the goods. I didn't feel this was one I could do off the cuff so the novel would have to go on hold. It would be a learning curve in itself and might help the writing bit. Anyway I had done very well in June.

I took myself into the mountains for a few days to work out a plan. I liked going into the mountains. Although July wasn't a going-into-the-mountains month. I decided that there was a likelihood that many members of the book club were themselves aspiring authors. Sure, they loved reading and loved their book club. Closet writers. Really what they wanted to do was put pen to paper themselves. So I thought that that should be my inspiration. I would introduce them to my experience over the last six months and how I had gone from 0 to 25,000 words. 25,002 to be precise.

I did think too that I should get a bit of help from those who had been around the block. Danny's book would be a starting point and maybe I'd find something in Malaga, there being no bookshop in the *sierras*. I took myself down to Malaga in search of a book shop. The city wasn't overrun with them. I found one on *Avenida Principal*. Its English language section was limited but, after a search, involving the pretty assistant on her knees, delivered up a book on writing by Ernest himself. Perfect.

I had a few hours to kill before my bus back so I tried the cathedral. Apart from other attractions, it was a welcome hiding place from the intense sun. Over the previous few days the temperature had begun to catch up on the season. As I stepped into the darkness, I could hear someone banging out Bach on the organ. There weren't a dozen people in the building, which is the size of a football pitch. What a privilege. A Bach concert all to myself. In Malaga Cathedral. A sheik couldn't fix that.

* * *

I have heard it said that the difference between an Irish witness and an English one is that an English witness wants to tell the truth, the whole truth and nothing but the truth, whereas an Irish witness just wants to give a good account of himself. This I certainly wanted to do and if there had to be a few porkies along the way then so be it. I was enjoying the exercise and, always ready to learn, finding out a lot about writing a novel as well. The three weeks passed quickly and in no time at all, apart from the three weeks of course, it was time to gather up my script and head for the meeting.

Jill and Reg kindly gave me a lift and, being OCD when it comes to punctuality, we arrived at the locked gates of the president's residence

half an hour before kick-off. It was only the book club she was president of but the security suggested a higher presidency. I jumped out of
the car and announced my name over the intercom.

"Who?" the voice with which I had established contact enquired.

I repeated my name.

"And what is the purpose of your visit?"

"I think if you ask the president she will be able to help you." This
was ridiculous.

"What's the problem?" asked Reg through the car window. "Are
they not expecting you?" Reg loved a little hitch.

"But surely you know the purpose of your visit?" the voice insisted.

"Of course I know the purpose of my visit." This didn't augur well
for the meeting. "This is *Villa Esperanza*, is it not?"

"No, it isn't. *Villa Esperanza* is on the other side of the street." The
intercom went dead.

In a matter of seconds we were whizzing through the open gates
of the residence to which we had been invited. The president gave us a
warm welcome, which was a relief. I was concerned that we were on
the early side and that she might not be ready for us. Indeed, might not
be up. I couldn't have been more wrong. The place had been buzzing
for hours. It felt as if we had entered an embassy.

The former Miss Northern Norway was utterly beautiful. I already
knew that. And utterly charming. I was confused. She brought us into a
comfortable room that had a wonderful view of the *sierras*.

"I'm sure you don't normally have a drink at this hour but I always
find that a little something settles the nerves and enhances performance", she said, handing me a *Carlos Primero*. Spanish measure.
"*Salud.*" *Salud* indeed. I hadn't been the slightest bit nervous up to that
moment but, now that she mentioned it, the *little something* was very
welcome. Down the hatch.

"*Sláinte*", I said.

I helped myself to another as my hostess led me to an alcove for an
even better view.

"There's something I must get off my chest before we start Mark."

I couldn't imagine what this might be.

"My email."

"Your email Dolores?" She wasn't giving much away. "What about your email?"

"It was quite rude."

"Not at all. What are you talking about? You're a busy woman."

"You see it was. You know it was. The fact is I didn't write it. It was my secretary. The secretary of the book club. Incoming president in fact. She's a bit of a cow."

"Think nothing of it."

"The fact is I would love to have met you. And I'm not that busy."

"You're very kind." I was warming to Dolores.

"Here, have another drop. I should have told you. We're not starting till half past. The mayor of Malaga is coming. He's a friend of mine and I thought he'd like your work." The mayor of Malaga. What a shame Helen wasn't here. She loves mayors. She had phoned the previous day to say that her plans had changed and she wouldn't be out for another week. I was a bit cross with her to be honest.

"But I thought you hadn't read my work?"

"I hadn't when I invited you but when you didn't get back to me, as I thought, I went ahead and looked you up on Amazon. I've read all your books in the meantime and I'm a huge fan."

"But you couldn't have. I haven't ...".

"Now, now, don't be modest."

"But there must be some mistake."

"No mistake. They're super and I can't wait to hear about the one you're working on at the moment. Speaking of which, I understand the mayor has arrived. Shall we?" I downed my *Carlos Primero tercero*, third, needing every drop of it. I had no idea what was going on but whatever misunderstanding there was, it wasn't going to be cleared up this side of my address. There was nothing for it but to go with the flow and, that being the decision, the *Carlos Primero* gave me a great advantage. I had never tasted Spanish brandy before. I would certainly taste it again.

I was conducted into what was nothing less than a small auditorium. I still didn't know what went on in this house apart from normal family activities, but it had to involve entertaining on a massive scale. You could almost fit the Berlin Philharmonic in the room. Apart from the size of the room, it was full. There must have been a hundred people there. All on their feet for my entrance. I had understood that this was a book club of fifteen or so members. The oldest book club in Andalucía must have grown since they last updated their website.

Dolores gave me a wonderful introduction. In fact, you could say, she was unstinting in her praise and gave my writing, which she had fallen in love with, her unqualified recommendation. It was odd sitting on the podium receiving this praise for my books which I hadn't written. I smiled.

I was a little unsteady rising to my feet. Three brandies, Spanish measure, before half past was considerably outside my comfort zone. However, with the exception of the president herself, who had matched me in consumption, and Reg and Jill, sitting in the front row, no one knew I had had anything other than the conventional coffee, so my unsteadiness was attributed to age, which I felt was harsh.

I had prepared a speech and thank God for that; indeed had gone to a lot of trouble doing so, including my trip to Malaga. There was only one thing for it. Let them have it. When I eventually got fully to my feet, I held my speech aloft, all ten pages of it, and, in Churchillian manner, waved it at my audience. I tore it up into quarters and let it fall to the floor. They loved it. Then, of necessity, I went off-piste as it were.

I have no recollection of what I said but I do know that I spoke and that it had all come together. The brandies and the mix-up should have drowned me. But they didn't. Somehow, the cocktail had liberated me. I was told afterwards that I treated the audience to amusing tales from the Four Courts in Dublin and followed that with an account of my five months to date in *Canillas* and my struggle with writing and light domestics. Apparently, I even mentioned the pancake. I didn't disabuse those present of the underlying lie, nor did I compound it.

I had decided before the day not to take questions but in the exuberance of the moment relented. "Big mistake", as Julia Roberts said to the assistants in the shop in Beverley Hills in *Pretty Woman*.

"Mr Barrington, I am interested in trying to write and what I would like to know of you as an established writer is, do you write what you think or what you think you think?"

"I beg your pardon?"

The aspiring writer repeated his question. The repetition was of no assistance. I was at sea. No idea what he was talking about.

Dolores, bless her, came to my rescue.

"I think what Oliver is asking you Mark [at that moment, the only Oliver I knew was Oliver Cromwell and look what he had done to us] is ..." and she went on to translate his question and answer it. I agreed wholeheartedly and, to a standing ovation, was whisked off the stage before I had a chance to advise him to change his name. Into the sanctuary from whence we came for more brandies and views of the *sierras*. Safe from the enquiring minds of aspiring authors.

* * *

I slept well.

Woken by the phone. Better than the doorbell.

"Mark, sorry to disturb you so early."

Where in the world is ten o'clock in the morning "so early"? Mexico maybe. Tibet.

"Dolores here. I'm sure you're at your desk." I wasn't at anything. "Have you been to Granada? What about lunch for a post-mortem. Yesterday was a great success and I'd love to go over it with you. I'll collect you at 12."

I didn't have an option as she had put the phone down, not rudely, before I had a chance to reply. I suppose she didn't get refusals. Anyway, I was free – still no sign of Helen – and wasn't in the mood for work. I was still high on how yesterday had gone. And of course the *Carlos Primeros*.

Her chauffeur-driven car arrived on the dot at the newly opened *Oficina de Turismo* alongside the bank that didn't have an ATM, and off we sped to Granada. An hour later she was ordering a bottle of wine on the terrace of the parador from where we looked into the gardens of the *Alhambra*. Some setting. Up to that moment, I only knew of it by reputation. I had hoped to get there sooner but these are the sort of sacrifices you have to make if you want to be a writer.

We clinked glasses.

"Thank you for yesterday Mark. You gave a great speech. Livened things up."

"No, no. Thank you. You saved my life at the end. I had no idea what that fellow was asking me."

"Nor had he. He's always asking esoteric questions. That's all he can do. He's from Scotland."

"But he's writing a book."

"He's no more writing a book than I am and, if he is, he'll certainly never finish it."

"Well thank you anyway. At that point, the brandies had landed and I was never going to be able to answer him."

"It's wonderful here, isn't it?" she said dreamily. She hadn't struck me as a dreamily sort of person. "My favourite place in Spain. And the *Mezquita* of course. But you can't have a glass of wine in the *Mezquita*."

"A drawback", I said.

"We have so much to be thankful to the Moors for." The Spanish or the expats? I didn't ask.

"Dolores, before we go any further, there is something I must say ...".

"No need Mark. I know."

"Know what?"

"That you didn't write those books."

"You know?"

"Yes."

"How do you know?"

"Because I made it up. I had to. That crowd wasn't going to listen to you if you hadn't got pedigree. And you hadn't. So I had to invent your pedigree. We're dealing in fiction aren't we? I knew you would be very good. I had made enquiries. But they still wouldn't have listened if you hadn't got stuff out there. Added to which, it was my big day and I wasn't going to let the fact that you weren't published ruin it. Not when I had already been let down by my good friend Donaldson."

"And what if someone wants to try and get it online?"

"They won't. Too mean. And if they do, it's out of print. Simple as that. And then they'll come and ask me and I'll say that there shouldn't be a problem and then they'll go away and forget all about it. Until of course this book comes out."

"Ingenious."

"Will we?" she asked, holding up the empty bottle.

"We can hardly just sit here talking", I said. No sign of our meal. One of the delights of Andalucía. *No pasa nada.* But, never arrive hungry to a Spanish restaurant.

We talked of life in Oslo and Dublin. Growing up. I told her I loved ABBA. "Sweden", she said. Her year as Miss Northern Norway. The Miss World itself in Tokyo. How close she had come. Some said it was fixed. Certainly political. How she had become a world ambassador for children though she had no children of her own. In the course of which she met her husband. An Olympic athlete who, fit as a fiddle, had died of a heart attack running the Melbourne marathon a few years earlier.

"That's it really. You know it all now. What about you? I've been doing all the talking. Do you enjoy the Law?"

"I do. But I have to admit that I've become a bit restless recently. Maybe I've run my course. And, as I said yesterday, the writing thing has always been tugging away. Ridiculous really. That length of time and yet it niggles."

"Very romantic", she said.

"I never thought of it like that."

"What about doing it full-time?"

"Steady on. I've only started."

"You don't have to be a bestseller. Write for the sake of it. Stay on. Write on."

"I'm not sure if Helen would want that."

"Who's Helen?"

"My wife. Didn't you know?"

"No. I thought you were here on your own."

"I am really. She wasn't able to come for the first six months but that's about to change."

"That'll be nice for you both. It can be lonely on your own."

"I hate being on my own. It's the one thing I don't like about being here. How do you manage? Though I can't imagine you being on your own for too long. It must have been very hard for you losing your husband like that?"

"It was. I still can't talk about it. In fact, I became quite a recluse for a few years. I suppose not having children made it more difficult. I'm just coming out of it really." She paused. "To be frank I was hoping that you were unattached. I thought you were."

"Thank you."

"You must have thought me very forward phoning you like that?"

"Not in the slightest. I was delighted to get the call. It's been a lovely lunch. I hope we'll do it again."

"Would you like a *Carlos Primero*? One for the road. The Spanish say *uno por el frio del camino*, one for the cold of the road."

"What a lovely expression. But it hardly applies in July? Anyway I'd love one. *Uno Por El Frio Del Camino*. It would make a nice title for a book."

"Maybe when you've finished this one and it's on its way, you will change your mind and stay and write another about your experience here and give it that title?"

"Nice idea. Who knows?"

"And you can come and address us again. And you won't need me to make you up."

"*Salud*" to that.

Two hours later, I was walking up *Calle Poeta Miguiñas* towards the *plaza*. Sun still high. Still hot. People had begun to come out of their houses for their *paseo*. The older folk were taking up the benches in the shade, chatting. *Buenas tardes. Buenas tardes.*

END OF MONTH REPORT

It was too much to hope for that the June momentum could be maintained. In the short term anyway. Perhaps the book club's invitation was a blessing in disguise. Give him a break from the writing and yet not wander too far. It is summer after all and it is hot. There is still time. However, a note of warning. It is imperative that the June momentum be picked up again and immediately. August must not be wasted.

9

AUGUST

Ten o'clock the following morning. Two mornings in a row at ten o'clock.

Surely not.

"Where on earth are you?" No apology this time.

Not.

"*En mi casa.* Where are you?"

"Malaga Airport."

"What are you doing in Malaga Airport?"

"Waiting for you"

"But you're not coming till the end of the week. *Fin de semana.*"

"Well I am. And I'm here. And would you please stop practising your Spanish on me. It's very irritating"

"Is it a surprise?"

"It is now. I spent the entire of yesterday trying to contact you. Spanish mobile. Irish mobile. Email. Where were you?"

"Eh, out. I was out."

"And your phones? Were they out too?"

"I left them behind."

"Did you not check them when you got in?"

The interrogation had gone on long enough.

"It's wonderful you're here. I haven't seen you since your birthday."

"I've been dying to come out and you don't even meet me."

"But I didn't know you were coming."

"Well if you answered your phones. One of them even."

"I'm sorry." I could hear her sobbing. "You stay where you are. I'll get the 3.30 down. I'll be with you at 5.30. And we'll spend the night in Malaga. This calls for a celebration. How come you're early?"

"Dawn flight."

"I didn't mean early in the day."

"Bit of a saga. Tell you when I see you. I got so pissed off yesterday that I booked this flight. Expensive too. I'm sorry."

"No sorry. It's great you're here. Just unfortunate I couldn't be at the airport to meet you. See you at 5.30. And if it's any consolation, you won't have any rain here between now and the end of the year."

Of course I was always going to meet Helen off the plane. It was the least she was entitled to. We had been apart for four months and it was the beginning of her adventure. She wasn't in any way a prima donna expecting a reception party every time she arrived home from a day's shopping. But clearly she was tired. Emotionally drained. For whatever reason. At the end of her tether. Wherever that is. From my point of view, knowing neither the day nor the hour, I couldn't meet her so there was no need for me to feel guilty. But I did feel that it would be better all-round if she didn't know that I had spent the day before on the edge of the *Alhambra* with Miss Northern Norway. Or vice versa. For the moment anyway. All in good time.

By 5.30, retail therapy under her belt, she was much better. By 7.30, we had checked into a good hotel nearby and were sitting in the sunshine on *Calle Larios* – we called it Grafton Street – sipping our gin and tonics and watching the *paseo* go by. The rain in Dublin far from her mind.

We ate in the shadow of the cathedral. It was still hot – too hot for bed – when we paid our bill so we went for a stroll around the old quarter. As luck would have it, groups of singers and dancers were popping up everywhere. The summer version of what we had been too tired to enjoy on our first night in February. We walked and talked. Danced and sang. I insisted Helen sit for a portrait artist. It was well after midnight, the streets teeming. Temperature more kind. A *Carlos Primero* ... *por el frio del camino* – I was a total convert – and a tango in a Buenos Aires bar before bed.

We had so enjoyed the night before we decided to spend another night in Malaga. Summer is its season.

On the third day we took the bus to *Canillas*.

We were barely in the door when the phone rang. Helen's this time. Jill welcoming Helen to the village and suggesting coffee at her earliest convenience and dinner for the four of us as soon as she had unpacked. In addition to the hand of friendship and welcome, Jill had a motive.

In time for summer the *Ayuntamiento* had put the finishing touches to a smart new tourist office, *Oficina de Turismo*, on the hill beside the bank. *Canillas* is a small village but there is no village too small for an *Oficina de Turismo*. Even *Archez* has one. According to Ian Gibson, an authority on Spain, in his book *Fire in the Blood*, the Spanish allocate their loyalty to village, district and country in that order. The villages are fiercely competitive and if the village down the road has a tourist office or a *piscina* or whatever, our village has to have one too. All the better if we can get in first. There is no need for *Canillas* to have an independent tourist office. The one in the neighbouring village of *Cómpeta* is more than capable of covering the needs of visitors to *Canillas*. But that's not the point. What is the point is that *Canillas* holds its head up high, high as *Maroma*, and that means having an *Oficina de Turismo*. And a number of other things besides.

Unfortunately, as soon as it was completed and opened to the public with a clamour of publicity – we weren't used to television cameras in *Canillas* – it closed. The *Ayuntamiento* couldn't afford to staff it. A public relations disaster for the newly elected mayor who had come in on a mandate for efficiency and good housekeeping. A white elephant was not what she needed. *Huevo* all over her face was quite sufficient.

She was on to Jill immediately: Jill, self-appointed representative of the English-speaking *extranjeros*. The word sounds a bit like strangers but means foreigners, if there's a difference. Wondering if she might be able to organise a temporary staffing of the new venture on a voluntary basis. Nothing Jill would like to do more. She was an organiser by nature and a bit of a politician into the bargain. She would have no difficulty marshalling the troops and would be delighted to have the popular new mayor beholden to her.

"What do you think Helen?" Jill asked that night over dinner.

"About what?"

"Joining the team."

"The tourist office?"

"Yes."

"No thanks."

"Why not?" The organising type never understands the not-to-be-organised-under-any-circumstances type.

"I've just arrived. I'm exhausted. And I don't know anybody."

"Nonsense, it'll be good for you. You'll get to meet people. You'll be a new person in no time."

"Jill's right", I threw in.

"I don't have any Spanish", Helen said, a clincher she thought. How could you work in a Spanish tourist office without Spanish?

"That's not true. You've more than me."

"That wouldn't be hard."

"You won't need any", said Jill.

"How come?"

"There won't be any tourists. It's August. This is walking territory. No one walks in August."

"Then why the tourist office?"

"I told you. *Cómpeta* has one."

"Oh very well." Jill and Reg had been very good to us since our arrival. "But only for you."

"You're a darling", said Jill, giving Helen a big kiss. I didn't even get a small one. I had turned down point blank the call to public duty on account of my novel. You have to put the foot down sometimes.

A week later, I went with Helen to the *Oficina de Turismo* for her first day. She was nervous, she said, and I was more familiar with the village and the area. An hour went by. Jill had been right. There wouldn't be any tourists.

Around midday, Jill arrived to see how it was all going. With the newly elected mayor, without *huevo* on her face, most welcoming and appreciative.

"Un cafe?" suggested the mayor. We had only been open an hour. I looked outside to see if there was any sign of a tourist. I was sure I'd heard a car. We put a 'BACK IN 20' on the door and crossed the road. Paco 1 was delighted to see us and insisted that coffee was on the house.

"I hope that the tourist office will be good for my business", Paco 1 said in Andaluz to the mayor, who translated into Spanish for Jill, who didn't understand anyway.

I said I'd go back and man the office.

As luck would have it – the first customer. An elderly couple from Madrid with not a word of English. They were on their way to Cordoba and wanted to book two tickets for the bullfight there the following week if there was a bullfight. I mean really. Some people are downright unreasonable. Imagine coming into a tourist office the size of a postage stamp in a mountain village with a request like that. We didn't even have a phone. It was just a place to pick up a plan of the village and information about restaurants. Of course, I was anxious to help. This was our first customer after all. But, how on earth was I to find out if there was a bullfight on in Cordoba the following week? I didn't even know if Cordoba had a bull ring. I had a brain wave. The mayor was in with Paco 1. I sent them in to her. They left without as much as a *gracias*, got straight into their 4x4 and drove off in the wrong direction. To be fair, there are no signposts in *Canillas*.

I didn't mention any of this to Helen. She wouldn't like a dissatisfied customer. Not on her watch. Another hour went by. As far as she was concerned, our first and, as it turned out, only visitor of the day.

A gentleman from Health and Safety. Or, so he claimed. As a result of my experience with the charming men not from the gas company, I was taking nothing for granted. I insisted on identification. All ok in that department. No imposters.

He wanted to check that everything was in order from the point of view of Health and Safety. He drew our attention to the fire extinguisher and left an accident and emergency kit with us. He filled out his form and told us that the new *Oficina* was performing very well. He was about to leave when he noticed something amiss. "*Madre mía*", he said, pointing to above the door through which he had entered a short while earlier and through which he was about to exit. Nothing amiss that we could see.

He was shaking his head. "No ..." he said. We got the "No" bit but just what went with the "No" we couldn't make out. At that point, he was talking to himself. Just when things had been going so well. We were puzzled. What might it be?

The counter was only a few strides from the door. Behind it, the staff chair for the *voluntario* on duty, a fan, a photocopier and a portrait of the new king. Then two more doors, one to a loo and the other to a storage space. Three in total, two of which in what might be called staff territory. The entire space not much bigger than my white room. And if two customers happened to turn up at the same time, one would have to form a queue outside.

With a circular motion of his hand, index finger extended, he indicated that he would be back. We indicated that we closed for the day at 2. "*No problema*", he said with a smile. "I come."

And "Come" he did. 2 on the dot. Bearing a sign. It would have been churlish of us on our first day to insist on the closing time. He had a small ladder with him and he set that up just inside the door. He climbed the small ladder with the sign under his arm so that we still could not see what the sign said. He wasn't hiding it. It was just the way he was climbing the ladder. When he got to the top of the ladder, he knocked a nail into the wall above the lintel, removed the sign from under his arm and hung it on the nail. The sign. Job done. 5 after 2. We hadn't been seriously delayed.

"*SALIDA*", the sign said proudly. Exit, in English. It didn't of course say EXIT in English or in any other language. Just "*SALIDA*".

"There", the gentleman from Health and Safety said. Or, the equivalent in Spanish. Clapping his hands, he stepped back to admire his handiwork. He was pleased. Job well done. A good note on which for him to go to lunch and for us to close the shop.

The Law had been invoked and the Law won. Should anything untoward occur in the *Oficina*, no one in the room at the time could be in the slightest doubt as to where the *salida* is. Certainly no one who understands Spanish. Nor, come to think of it, anyone who is able to use the two eyes God or Darwin has given them.

Helen completed her first day in the office by recording in the diary the visit of the gentleman from Health and Safety. No mention of the *Cordoba 2*. Not another tourist in sight.

* * *

Emilio is my best friend in *Canillas*. He owns one of the two hotels in town. Two hotels. Not bad for such a small place. It's a lovely hotel. No frills. He runs it on his own because he has difficulty holding onto staff. He also has difficulty holding onto guests but this is because he doesn't have staff. He is an award-winning chef (they say chef too but they pronounce it *chef* not *shef* like we do) with a temperament to go with it. Being such a good chef, he does not need assistance in the kitchen. But he sure needs it elsewhere. For example, in the service area. Regulars know they will get a beautiful meal but don't know what time they will get it. Better not to arrive hungry. The key: arrive looking forward to a drink or two or three, with no interest in food for the time being, and, as the drink or two or three and time pass, allow the hunger catch up. Even that doesn't always work.

Emilio is an artist, trapped in a sumo-wrestler's body, and wears a dentist's shirt which could be cleaner. What he is interested in is producing exquisite food, thereby giving his customers a memorable culinary experience. He has no interest in the business end of things and no interest in profit. And probably doesn't make any. Indeed he doesn't really want to charge at all. When it comes to bill time, he arrives at your table with a paint brush and, with a flourish, writes the bill on the paper table-cloth, in the process beating you down.

"No, no, no, you couldn't possibly have had two *gin tónicas* and certainly not three", he insists. "Alright, half a bottle of wine [the bottle is empty]; I won't charge you for the vegetables and the *postre* is on the house." If you offer a service charge, he gets offended and points out that there is no staff to receive it. Emilio is an endangered species.

For the few who have the time and are prepared to put up with his eccentricity, an amazing culinary experience is in store. Invariably, he joins you towards the end of your meal with his own glass of wine and gives an eloquent commentary on the sun going down.

The grandchildren were about to come among us. Again. I had already lost my white room and the "DO NOT DESTERB" sign, created and placed on the door by eldest grandchild at Easter, had been restored to its wrongful place. Once again, my novel was in trouble. Even if the opportunity for writing presented itself in the month ahead – unlikely – I had nowhere to go. In short, I had been evicted.

"Emilio", I said one evening when he had finished his dissertation on the sunset, "would you have a room in your hotel which I could use during August?" It wasn't quite as easy as this to get my question across as neither of us yet were fluent in the other's language. But we were coming along.

"*Mi amigo*", he said, putting his arm around my shoulder – the Spanish are a tactile lot – "for you, anything." I explained about the grandchildren and my white room and the fact that I had been thrown out. He knew about the book. "You must have a place to write", he said, or something like it. "As we Spanish like to say, *mi hotel es tu hotel*. This month I have empty rooms. The walking season is over until October and most of the people coming here are returning for the holidays to their families."

"*Estupendo*", I said. "You are a true friend. But, Emilio this has to be on a professional basis." My Spanish was coming along.

"*Claro*", he said, "but we can talk about that later. The thing *importante* is that you write."

* * *

Helen was settling in. Her six-month sabbatical couldn't have come at a better time. The heat was the downside. The south of Spain was in the grip of a heat wave and poor Helen had arrived in the middle of it. At least I had had an opportunity to acclimatize. Not that it gave me much of an advantage. We had been warned. July and August unbearable. Even the Spanish were moaning. "*Mucho calor*", mantra of the day.

It had been manageable up to the end of June. If anything, spring had been a disappointment. It was as if someone had turned on the heat on the first of July. Perhaps for *Feria*. Simply turned on a little tap somewhere and out poured the heat. Day by day, hotter and hotter. I'm not sure if it can get hotter exponentially but that's how it felt

Now August was well and truly here. Temperatures had soared. High thirties. One night in the *plaza*, thirty-five degrees at midnight. I appreciate that it's hotter in the Sahara but we hadn't chosen to live in a desert. We couldn't sleep by night. We couldn't sleep by day. The air conditioning was broken and all the fan did was move the flies about. We tried getting up early. We tried getting up late. Nothing worked. The elders sat on benches around the village till the early hours. Some took their chairs out and watched television from the street. It was all a monumental waste of time. August is indeed a wicked month.

The sun went to work about seven. And carried on working until nine or ten at night. The entire day. Without a break. Without a cloud. We hadn't seen a cloud since May. The heat peaking in the long-drawn-out afternoon. You could smell it. It filled your nostrils. No one, nothing, moved, especially not the cat in the sleepy garden. Mostly I didn't go out before five, when I went to the pool.

To say the village comes alive in August would be an exaggeration. But, by its own standard of desertedness during the rest of the year, it is relatively accurate. Windows, shuttered all winter, suddenly thrown open. Out-of-condition clothes lines sag with the weight of new washing. Roof terraces fill with conversations. The perfume of *dama de noche* yields to the barbecue. There are people about.

Including our little ones and their parents, whom we tucked into a small villa on the edge of the village, overlooking *Archez*, whose illuminated minaret rises to the stars like a candle from a cake.

* * *

The *zambomba* is a musical instrument. Though you wouldn't know to look at it. It consists of a container and a stick. The container is a ceramic jar that you might put a plant in if you weren't going to use it as a *zambomba*. It is covered with the stretched skin of a goat, which has a small hole in the middle for the stick. The musician holds the remains of the goat with one hand and thrusts the stick in and out of the hole with the other in a rhythmical manner, thereby producing a musical experience.

Our friend and neighbour Lourdes is the leading exponent of the *zambomba* in the village.

We were sheltering in the house one mid-afternoon when there came a knock on the door. Due to the heat, we were in a state of undress unfit to receive visitors. Helen jumped into the downstairs bathroom. There is only one bathroom and it's downstairs. I flew upstairs where I threw on a towel and returned to the open area where Lourdes had already taken up her position. She had refined her modus operandi from earlier in the year. Whereas before she knocked twice and went for the door handle, giving us some chance; now, in the interest of time management, she only knocked once and went for the door handle, giving us no chance at all. How we had got to bathroom and upstairs respectively I don't know.

She was on her own. No avocados. No soap. She was upset. Unlike her. Normally, full of smiles and incomprehensible chat. *Qué tal?* She showed me her *zambomba*. The ceramic jar was without cover. In which condition, it could not be played. She had removed the goat skin from the container for some reason and, like a tight skirt, she couldn't get it back on. It required strength to stretch the goat skin and at the same time tie it with string to the rim of the container and at eighty-five she didn't have that strength. Into the bargain, she was performing that evening in the *plaza*. At least that is what I thought she told me. What was she going to do? She was the leader of the *zambombians*. At this point, she took a piece of paper as if to write a letter of resignation. Helen, following events from the bathroom and, having a better grasp of Lourdes' Andaluz, decided it was now or never and emerged from the bathroom with her towel and an apology. We needed her and, in particular, her dexterity. Between the three of us we got it done and restored the smile to the leader's face.

She was once more eager for action. Helen, with one hand on her modesty, poured Lourdes a cup of tea with the other. We had saved the day. The concert could go ahead and Lourdes could lead her *zambombians*. We went along of course. There was a smile on her face the width of the Mediterranean. She gave us a wink and a thumbs up – the non-playing thumb. The least we could do after all the avocados and soap.

* * *

Cómpeta Feria at the end of July lasts five days. Enough for one summer, you might think. Two weeks later, she's off again. *Noche del Vino*, another hardy annual. Why *Noche* I don't know. It kicks off at eleven in the morning. Why *Vino* I don't know either. It is *Cómpeta's* celebration of the Assumption of Our Lady into Heaven and, apart from Our Lady's request for a miracle at Cana, I don't associate her with alcohol. A national and international celebration but nowhere with as much gusto as in *Cómpeta*. I had assumed that the *Noche del Vino* bit was a Spanish thing or at least Andalucían. Apparently not. It belongs to *Cómpeta*. In the twenty-first century, a twenty-four-hour celebration of the Queen of Heaven in a mountain village in the south of Spain.

Mass of course. There's a lot of Mass in the mountains. A packed church and a super choir. Women in full costume. Midday, we spilt out into the sunshine where *Cómpeta's* municipal band took over from the choir. The band played us around the village, along its streets, winding also, through a market of arts and crafts and farm produce for the occasion.

Not to mention two pigs whose arrival in the *plaza* we had witnessed earlier. Being a city lad, I don't know if pigs have a sense of dignity but, if they have, it got a severe jolt this day of celebration. They were taken from a van and shunted on their front legs at speed as in a wheel-barrow race, except they were perpendicular to the ground. Not happy campers. We thought they were making their last journey and so did they. We were relieved, and so were they, to find them guzzling contentedly in a trough of tomatoes alongside a Spanish group all dressed up singing *'Nessun Dorma'*. We walked on to *Plaza Vendimia*. It was then I realised that the day was double-booked, Our Lady sharing with the harvesting of the grapes.

First, a presentation of awards. Boring. We weren't getting any. And the sun shone down. Then, the treading of the grapes, the traditional way of making wine. Sandalled *pisadores* in peasant costume stamping on the grapes to music as the juice ran out. I did know that in some corners of the world, as part of the manufacturing process, cigars are rubbed between a woman's thighs. I didn't know that the beautiful grapes that make beautiful wine are first beaten black and blue by peasants in sandals. It's not the peasant bit I take exception to. Why not squeeze the grapes between the woman's thighs? As this was going on, falcons were swooping from one side of the *plaza* to another an inch above our heads. Music played, revellers danced. *Fiesta* lunch consisted of a McDonald's-size portion of *migas*, a frightful looking thing – resembling crumbs but less interesting – and a glass of local wine.

Día del Vino was well under way. *Noche* still to come.

Plaza Almijara takes its name from the local mountains. It consists of a church, three restaurants, an art gallery and two clocks that have stopped at different times. It is bigger and busier than our *plaza* in *Canillas*, which has only one clock and tells the correct time. I had seen it in rain. I had seen it in mist. I had seen it empty. Mostly I had seen it in sunshine. When we arrived this August evening at nine o'clock for our reservation, the *plaza* was packed to capacity. A stage had been erected for the performance and the remaining area had been filled with seats which were available from the *Ayuntamiento* for three Euro. Including a hat, a fan and a poster boy with a basket of grapes on his head, the theme for this year's *Noche*. The seats were tied together in case you were minded to take them home with you.

We could have watched the performance from our table outside the restaurant when we had finished our meal but as we had paid for the tickets we decided to move closer to the stage. The performance had already started. Our seats had to be in the middle of the row which was in the middle of the auditorium and we had to disturb everyone in order to get to them. And when we got to them they were occupied. A Spanish family. Elderly couple, man with stick, and young couple with sleeping baby. What a target. We showed them our tickets. Had they been German, we could have mentioned all those towels left out at pools at six in the morning in resorts around the world. Had they shown the slightest resistance, we'd have moved on. Eventually we were seated. For a while I was distracted by the Spanish family and the easy manner in which they had taken their eviction. 700 years of occupation by the Moors, I supposed.

I settled down.

A flamenco quartet.

A beautiful woman with a beautiful voice tugging at her long black dress in a frenzied manner as if trying to take it off.

Perhaps just cross with the woman in the shop who sold her a size too small.

A gentleman, also in black, playing Spanish guitar.

A flamenco dancer defying the laws of human movement,
twisting and turning so fast
dexterity
hauteur
insinuating her hands
and fingers
into the air
stamping her feet
– I know no dance like it –
lifting her dress
showing her thigh
back so straight
head so high
all the time
her fingers intertwining
as the branches of a bonsai.

It was electric. I was on my feet. On my way to join her on the stage. When Helen returned me to my seat. Sure I couldn't even do the hokey-cokey.

The door on the stage flung open. Enter He for whom we had been waiting. The fourth member of the quartet. *El Maestro*. Pencil-thin and tall, he had to be all of seventy. He bestrode the stage like an Olympian. Belying his years. He too stamped his feet, twisted and turned. One hand gyrating above his head, the other behind his back, he clicked his fingers and he clicked his heels. As tall and straight as the clock tower behind him. Nothing wrong with his timing. Nor his beat.

Together they danced apart,
mercilessly.
Relentlessly.
Sweat pouring from the stage.
Like the wine from the grapes.
In the end, the audience stood and stood.

It was late, not over, when we took our leave. It seemed right that the people whose place this is should have some time to themselves. As I made my way home, it dawned on me that the day was not all about Our Lady. The grapes were there too.

* * *

It was the middle of August and I had written hardly a word since my purple patch in June. I was like a golfer in search of his second major. One didn't make a reputation. *Feria* had given way to Miss Northern Norway's invitation which in turn gave way to Helen's arrival and then the children. During the excitement of *Noche del Vino* I resolved to take up Emilio's offer of a writing room the very next day.

Probably not the best morning for the resumption of creative duties. The morning after, after all.

"Marco, where have you been? *No te he visto*. I haven't seen you. *Mucho tiempo*." Emilio greeted me like a long-lost friend. It had only been a few days. "*Tu libro*."

"I know Emilio. Busy ... *muy* busy ... *familia* ... *dificile* ... *chicas* ... *imposible*."

"No excuses, Marco. *Tu quieres* great writer, *necesita escribir*. You want great writer, you must write. *Mi papa* always said to me,

'Emilio,' he said, 'you want great chef, you must in kitchen.' Same for you Marco." With which advice he led me to an open room off the foyer – a lovely room with a view to the mountains, you just can't get away from them – and disappeared.

He was back in a few minutes with a *café solo*.

"You need this", he said.

It worked but not for long. When he returned an hour later, I was asleep.

"Marco?" he wanted to know. "What's up?"

"*Qué calor*", I replied. "The heat."

"I don't think so", he said, "*Noche del Vino*, more likely. Very drinking. I think you no write today." He had a point. "*Va a la piscina. Trabaja mañana*." With which he led me to the entrance to his hotel and turfed me out. *Mi amigo bueno*.

* * *

It is at the *piscina* that the difference between *Canillas* in summer and *Canillas* during the rest of the year is most obvious.

For nine months, the pool lies empty. There is a bar there and it does a small pizza and beer business all year round. For young people. In the inner temple of the pool room, a poster of a woman in a thong, bending half-way across a pool table to take her shot, looks out of place during family time in August. I doubt if Angeles, whose son – a different son – runs the bar, has seen the poster. Other posters are less in your face. Abbey Road. Marilyn Monroe. Brooklyn Bridge. The swimming pool opens from mid-June to mid-September, in line with the school holidays, and, like the village, comes into its own in August. Most afternoons we were there. We wouldn't have survived without it.

Most days it was busy. Spaniards home for the holidays. A few French who had driven down. "The Pyrenees are gone" Philip II declared, a bit previously, in 1578. Four hundred years later, they sure are. A sprinkling of Northern Europeans and a few locals. Young locals. The elders don't come near the place. Their preference: a bench in the shade in the village.

The pool was supervised by a young woman with the lovely name of Amable, meaning kind, more intent on practising her English on anyone who was prepared to listen than watching the swimmers. Early on in our relationship she told me she had an exam coming up. *Necesario* for her to work very hard – I thought she was going to say for the next year or two but no – for the next two weeks. This wasn't easy because she did babysitting in the morning, lifeguarding in the afternoon and preparing the meal for her family in the evening. After all that, she was really quite exhausted and it was a bit difficult to put in the three hours study that her teacher said was *absolutamente necesario*. Reading the situation, I suggested thirty minutes as a practical compromise but, upon reflection, she was inclined to think that she was too tired even for that.

She said she was going to tell the mother of the children whom she babysat that she could stuff her babies and her own family that they could sing for their supper. I told her she was quite right to take these steps but I had a sneaking suspicion that while she would continue to tell me how *necesario* it was for her to work hard for the two weeks remaining, she would still find that when the time came to work hard she would be too tired. She was, after all, from *Andalucía* and it was very hot.

We built up quite a rapport and each day when Helen and I came down for our swim I would spend an amount of time with Amable and her "redactions", with which, frankly, she was obsessed. While Helen read her book. Amable was fond of the word and kept referring to her latest redaction. I was puzzled because it wasn't a word we used when I was at school in Dublin in the sixties. I came to the conclusion that it was a sort of essay, sort of. She was given a topic and she had to write a number of sentences on it. For example, she had written a number of sentences on the topic of both parents working full-time. "It is difficult", she wrote, "for both parents to work full-time because the mother wants to be at home breastfeeding and the father has to teach his child values." Charming and all as the sentiment is, I was taken aback by how old-fashioned it sounded and wondered if Franco had written it. Entirely hers, apparently.

Part of the exercise was pronunciation and the word she had most difficulty with was "breastfeeding." She just couldn't get her Andalucían tongue around it. So, there we were the two of us, at the edge of the pool, me in my togs in my sixties, she in her bikini lite, repeating the word "breastfeeding" ad something or other.

One afternoon I swam over to her side of the pool. It wasn't very far. To ask her if she had done her homework the night before. The Spanish word for homework is *deberes* apparently so I asked her if she had done her *deberes*. It was only a pleasantry and I only expected a pleasantry back. But, for Amable, this was another chance to practise her English. She left her seat, where she was keeping one eye on the swimmers and two on her redactions. I was standing in the pool on my tippy toes, just about keeping my nose above water. She dropped to her knees and leant over me to practise her English. The lesson continued, the two of us maintaining our respective positions. This was no bother to me because the sun was hot and the water not cold. After all, I had spent my summers in Blackrock Baths and watched sea-swimmers on Christmas Day. So she began to tell me about her latest redaction and what she had written and as she did I made a few helpful suggestions. Also, I said I wouldn't mind seeing more of her redactions but she said that she had left them at home, which I thought was a bit odd. And we threw in a few pronunciations to keep our tongues in as it were. This was all fine and I think must have been of some value to Amable. And of course I wasn't cold. There was, however, what I might call a logistical difficulty. Just visualise for a moment.

I'm in the water on my tippy toes just keeping my nose out of it. Nonchalantly resting my arms on the side of the pool like an under-graduate. Amable, for her part, in a bikini two sizes too small for her, is leaning over me in a sort of 'S' position, like some sort of contortion out of a Picasso painting, her head almost in the water. Our positions lead to certain unavoidables. One anyway. There is only one way for me to look. At her. And looking at her I can't avoid looking at a certain part of her. All the time we're chatting away about her redactions. She is utterly unflapped. I'm utterly the opposite. I can't help noticing that she has quite big redactions. Not Raquel Welch mind. Just quite big. I try my best to look away a few times but I get the distinct feeling when I do that that she thinks I am losing interest in her. And after all we have her exam to think of.

It all worked out in the end because after about fifteen minutes of looking, I mean redactions, Helen came over and rescued me. She has a great instinct that way.

So for a while Helen and I concentrated on the swimming lesson for the youngsters. Manolo is the star. He is four, going on five. As soon as he arrives, his arms go straight up in the air for the instructor to take off his T-shirt. Then he goes over to the shower. Difficult for him to turn the knob but eventually he manages it. Out pours the water. He tilts his head forward so a few drops land on the crown of his head and that's the shower done. Off he runs to the kiddies pool. Stands at the edge and sizes the whole thing up. Only a few days earlier, he had been a reluctant beginner. Today, a convert with all the zealotry that that entails.

He turns his back on the small pool and runs across grass for about thirty yards to a wall which is the furthest point from the pool. There he stops and turns around. This marks the beginning of his run-up. Like for a long-jumper, the idea of the run-up is to gather speed so that at the moment of lift-off you have optimum momentum. Manolo wouldn't be able to articulate all of this but he has worked it out for himself by instinct. By instinct he knows that to achieve the most satisfying jump into the small pool, he needs to have covered sufficient ground to give him maximum speed at lift-off.

Now to implement the theory. First of all he holds his nose. There isn't any need for him to hold his nose for the entire of the run-up. It will be quite sufficient for his purpose, to prevent water going up his nose, for him to hold his nose for the first time as he makes his leap. Manolo doesn't know that so, at the wall, beginning his run-up, he is already holding his nose. Thirty yards to go. Going well. Gathering speed. The holding-the-nose bit slowing him a little. Onwards and, hopefully, upwards. Destined to be the best jump of his career to date. For some reason when he reaches the edge, travelling as fast as his fatty legs can carry him, the very point where he should take off, he stops, stops dead, bends his knees and from the very stationary point of dead, he jumps into the pool with a big roar and a smile. The entire run-up a complete waste of time.

Amable wasn't finished. She didn't give up that easily. The final redaction of the day.

"I think you should take out the word 'moreover' at the beginning of that paragraph", I suggested. She was happy to do so and with her rubber erased the word.

"If you can think of another word instead that would make my redactions more beautiful, that would be good", she said, smiling.

"Your redactions are fine", I said, "quite fine."

Helen jumped in.

" Time for *gin tónica* Mark."

"*Hasta luego*", Amable said. "Till tomorrow. In the meantime, I have new listens", referring to her audio, 'English in Two Weeks'.

Of course you have darling.

* * *

That's how we got through August. More or less. Crawling around naked during the day, reading a page or two, writing not at all – I bet you Hemingway never wrote a word in August – listening to Bob Dylan, washing a mug when we needed a cup of tea. When we thought it might be safe to venture out, we headed for the pool, taking advantage of every shape of shade along the way. Around eight we would order a pizza and watch the sun go down.

END OF MONTH REPORT

None available due to annual leave.

10

SEPTEMBER

Overnight, the temperature dropped. Now it didn't go down to zero. But it dropped. A cloud. A cooling breeze. Something to be grateful for. As if, taking advantage of the absence of day, whoever is in charge of these things had nudged the tap through which the heat had poured relentlessly for the previous two months. A blip possibly. Possibly, a beginning of an end. An end to the intensity of the Andalucían summer. Either way, most welcome.

End of summer told me that deadlines, dreaded deadlines, were on their way. July had been sacrificed to the book club. August to the heat. I hadn't got back to Emilio's. End of year not far away. Time to put the head down big time. September now a crucial month. 122 writing days to Christmas.

Back to the Great Novel. Back to Ben. Within a week of making the decision, he had packed his toothbrush, arranged a sabbatical with the *Irish Times* – maybe, a weekly column – and was on a flight to *Cádiz*. Where he hired a car and drove down the *Costa de la Luz* until he found a village where he could settle at least for a while. All he wanted was a room, a bar or two nearby and a view of the Mediterranean. Two out of three. He was on the wrong side of the southern tip for the Mediterranean. He got the Atlantic and a three-sided plaza that opened onto it. Needless to say, within a week of unpacking his toothbrush he was back on the sauce.

He had been a courageous war correspondent, most recently in Afghanistan. Adventure and danger his trademarks. For the previous year, he had worked from Dublin. He was a solitary type, keeping himself to himself and his beautiful wife. And, of course, now she was no longer with him. So, what else was he to do in this coastal village but have a bottle of wine over lunch staring out at the ocean, followed by a siesta and more of the same as the sun went down?

He had been through a bad few months on the romantic front and, while fully intent on the writing, it was too early to begin. He allowed himself a month and then he would set to. A novel, he decided. It had to be a novel. The editor of the *New Yorker*, who admired his short stories, told him so. No one buys short stories he told him. To his surprise. He thought that short stories were the perfect medium for an age in which no one had any time.

So, a month in which to work out a story for a novel, drink plenty of red wine and stare at the ocean.

I now had two plots to fix:

What was going to happen to Ben?

What was Ben going to write about?

Clock ticking.

This called for a new timetable. Into the China shop in *Cómpeta* – they're everywhere – where I bought myself a small blackboard and some chalk. In the process interrupting a Skype call between the shopkeeper and her family in Shanghai. Back in the white room, I proceeded to write the salient dates on the board.

First, the months.
A box for each month.
Rest of September,
October,
November,
December,
January.
In theory, five.
Five boxes.

Working backwards, my year wasn't up till the end of January so *End of Year* went in the January box with 31st in brackets. But that would be leaving it to the last minute. In addition, having given the matter due consideration, I decided that, Christmas being Christmas and me being me, nothing would get done during the festive season. So, *Christmas* went in the December box and *Post-Christmas* joined *End of Year* in the January one.

In reality, three.

What about *Tweaking* and *Looking for a Publisher*? November.

Leaving me with Rest of September and October. Less than two months to complete.

This exercise had not been a waste of time. I was a great believer in planning. It had focused the mind and brought me up against an unassailable truth. The one redeeming feature was that I had been here before. Back in May. And I had gone to my guru who did not fail me. Ruthlessness he had said then. More Ruthlessness it had to be now. I wrote it on the blackboard in capital letters.

MORE RUTHLESSNESS

It was by no means certain that with more ruthlessness there was enough time. What was certain was that, without it, the project was doomed. The path forward was clear.

However, as one of the most famous people of the twentieth century said, "Life is what happens to you while you're busy making other plans." An updating of *the best laid schemes* I suppose.

"Mark, *plaza*, we've got to talk." This was unusually summary of Helen. Ten minutes later we were ordering a bottle of wine. Unusual too. Helen didn't drink during the day.

"I can't stay Mark", Helen announced.

I had just said cheers and was in the act of taking my first sip. The top half of my glass of red wine – I can't be certain it was all from the top half – crossed the table, landing on Helen's white blouse and pearly breasts. The rest I nearly choked on.

"You can't what?"

Visitors at nearby tables looked up.

"You heard me, I can't stay."

"What do you mean you can't stay? You're joking, aren't you?"

"I wish I were."

"What's the problem? I thought you liked it here. Settling in nicely. It's the heat. That's what it is. But we've turned the corner. It's going to cool down. You'll love it."

"It's not just the heat, Mark. It's everything. I don't know what we're doing here."

"I'm writing a book and you're working in the tourist office."

"I am not working in the tourist office. I was just helping Jill out. I've resigned."

"Well, you're on holiday then, and, if I may say so, a well-earned holiday."

"Don't patronise me Mark. I know all that but I'm lonely. I miss the little ones. I miss home. And the heat is unbearable."

"That's changing. I told you. Why didn't you say all this when we were at your sister's?"

"I didn't know then."

"You said you wouldn't go West. You didn't say you wouldn't come out here."

"I didn't want to go anywhere. I was happy at home. I only came out here because you were so keen."

Oh dear.

"You're serious then?"

"I'm sorry."

"It's not a question of sorry."

This wasn't helpful. This was a joint venture. It wasn't all about me. Before it even began, the joint bit had been reduced by 50 per cent. Now it was to disappear altogether. At least she hadn't told me she was a lesbian. I had another go. I was a barrister after all. Trained to persuade.

"I won't be able to do it without you", I tried.

"Nonsense", her reply. That wasn't her opinion back in January. "For heaven's sake, you've written nothing since I arrived."

"I did an hour in Emilio's the day after *Noche del Vino.*"

"Mark."

"That wasn't you. That was the heat. No one could write in that heat. Not even Hemingway. And anyway it's cooling down. I'll race through it. Only another 25 to go, give or take."

"25 what?"

"Words. 25,000 words."

"25,000?"

"Maybe a bit more."

"That'll take forever."

"I've already written 25, remember. I know where I'm going. Nothing to it. If you leave me now ... well ... I'll be lonely and maybe I won't be able to finish it. It was very difficult out here on my own."

"You can always go back to the *Alhambra.*"

What?

"Is that what this is all about?"

"It certainly isn't but why didn't you tell me?"

"Tell you what?"

"About your date in the *Alhambra* with Miss World."

"She isn't Miss World and it wasn't a date. I didn't tell you because there was nothing to tell."

"You told me all about your day at the book club."

"Of course I did."

"But not a word about the *Alhambra.*" This was ridiculous.

"This is ridiculous", I said. "Dolores rang me the morning after the meeting. She was pleased with how her final meeting as president had gone and thought we might have lunch in the parador to celebrate her retirement. She put the phone down before I had a chance to refuse.

I was going to write that day as I had lost a lot of time. We had a lovely lunch over a bottle of wine. That's all there is to it. We didn't go back to her place and I was in our bed by ten o'clock. In fact, the last thing she said to me was that we must do it again with you once you had settled in."

"Now that you've got that off your chest ..." I let it go. "... maybe we could get back to the real item on the agenda."

"If you're adamant, would you think of going home for a few weeks and coming back when you're feeling better?" Oh dear. "Feeling better." Not great. Helen was in like a lynx.

"I'm not sick Mark."

"No, no. I know that but what do you think of the suggestion?"

"I think we should just see how we both feel after a break." I didn't like the sound of this. We'd had a break. Six months of a break. I didn't think I should go there. *Poco a poco* as they say here.

With that, we returned to our house for a siesta. *Sin nata.*

Coming on the very day that I discovered I had less than two months in which to finish my book, Helen's timing was impeccable. Not that the timing changed things. She didn't waste any time. That evening, she booked her flight, one way, for *pasado mañana*, the day after tomorrow.

* * *

In one jurisdiction, a Kiwi is an All-Black. In another, it is a humble fruit. My next-door neighbour in Dublin wouldn't know a rugby ball from a kiwi. His passion is the garden. He is what is known as 'a keen gardener'.

During August, I had received from him a text. A peremptory text.

"A kiwi by the end of the month", the text said succinctly.

My neighbour: a master of succinctness and the peremptory. Legacies of a life in the army. Coming from this source, there could be no ambiguity. A kiwi could mean only one thing.

Nothing to it, I had thought. Rustle up a few local kiwis at the Saturday morning market before we next go home. Though why he couldn't just walk to his local fruit shop I didn't know.

"How many would you like?" I replied, tapping into his passion for precision, another army hangover.

"What do you mean, how many would I like? One kiwi plant is all I am looking for. No excuses. End of the month." Precision, succinctness and the peremptory all in one text.

"A plant? Of course. I thought you wanted me to bring home some kiwi fruit."

No reply.

The task seemed to come within my capacity. I didn't think that you could grow kiwis in Ireland but that was for him. I was simply the messenger.

Now that Helen was going home early and as she had a day to spare, I suggested tentatively that we carry out this instruction. I was not at all sure how this would go down. To my relief, she jumped at it. A project perhaps. Something we could do together. Something neutral that wouldn't make demands on us emotionally. We had had enough of that the day before.

With that, we called on a gardening centre in the *campo*. It was well-stocked and the lady who dealt with us was charming, if without English. I don't know why I mention she is 'without English' as if she should be 'with English'. This is a mountain village in Spain after all. Why on earth should I expect her to speak English? You mightn't find English in a mountain village in England.

Even after being here for 0.67 of a year, I had little Spanish. Which I attributed to my project. Early on, I decided that, the book being my priority, learning the language could not get the attention it deserved. There is only so much that you can fit into a day after all.

Helen, on the other hand, had a little more. If not as much more as she thought. Being an au pair in Madrid for six weeks the summer after she had left school gave her an advantage. I didn't think it would matter – not that she had been an au pair in Madrid – but that she didn't have as much Spanish as she thought. The task seemed straight-forward. The purchase of a kiwi plant in a gardening centre shouldn't require too great a knowledge of the language.

However, that assumption was not taking into account the fact that Helen had learnt her Spanish in Madrid. Castillian Spanish. BBC

Spanish as it were. Very different from what we have here. Here in the mountains in the south, they speak even more quickly than elsewhere in Spain and, in the process, drop at least half of the words they are purporting to use. The result? Another language altogether.

Being the sort of person who thinks ahead, I consulted my dictionary – Collins ... Pocket ... Spanish ... in Colour – to find out what the word for 'kiwi' is ... and yes ... it is ... 'kiwi'. When I look up a dictionary for translation purposes, having looked up the word, in this instance 'kiwi', in the English section and found that the Spanish word is 'kiwi', I then look up 'kiwi' in the Spanish section, as a sort of double-check, only to find that it's not there.

In any event, "that's it", I thought to myself, "job done." All that was required was to turn up at the garden centre, utter the magic word 'kiwi' and Roberto's your uncle. Actually his name is Alfredo.

"Kiwi", I announced triumphantly, in the manner of a returning conquistador. I wasn't going to be messed with. Even though Helen had more Spanish, I felt that I should lead. It was a simple request I thought, simply stated, and certainly didn't call for the rant – albeit charming – that followed. Her reply took as long as the Sunday sermon and confirmed that Helen's summer as an au pair had been a complete waste of time and her father's money. We looked at one another in incomprehension. Then, in case our incomprehension was unclear to the charming Spanish lady without English, we muttered "no comprendo" in unison.

Helen decided to take over. She kept repeating "DESPACHO". To no avail. The lady didn't serve soup, I thought to myself. She surely thought Helen was saying "GASPACHO". She should have been saying "DESPACIO" – SLOW DOWN.

After a while, the charming Spanish lady without English (I will refer to her as CSLWE – after all we've all got homes to go to) decided unilaterally that there was no point in discussing the matter further and signalled us to follow her outside, to the kiwi department.

Things were looking arriba.

Only briefly.

The kiwi plants were 3-feet tall.

"How on earth can I bring these on Ryanair?" Helen asked a taken-aback CSLWE. Hardly her department.

"And even if I can, am I allowed to?" Helen's background is a mixture of law and medicine and she didn't like what she had heard of the *Guardia Civil.* The CSLWE's taken-abackness worsened.

I decided to bring things down to earth.

"S-M-A-L-L-E-R?" I asked phonetically. Demonstrating at the same time. Who said men can't multi-task? Why I thought she might follow phonetic pronunciation of an English word I don't know but she did understand my demonstration and answered "NO" in both languages.

We were stuck. No option but to buy a 3-foot kiwi and hope for the best with Ryanair.

We were counting our chickens, if not our kiwis.

Another rant, in the course of which it became clear that if we wanted one, we had to have two. A new marketing technique as far as we were concerned. Grossly unfair, we told her, and in breach of our consumer rights under EU law. She wasn't for turning.

She took one kiwi plant, then another and laid them bare on the floor of the garden centre. She started fiddling with them in a fiddling sort of way until eventually we realised what she was at. By means of horticultural artistry, she was showing us that kiwi plants have gender. Like us, there is a male and a female and you can't have one without the other. "That's what I was trying to tell you", she seemed to say. We smiled and said *"comprendo"* and *"gracias"* repeatedly.

Almost there. Kiwi saga almost complete. One final hurdle, ill-advised, as I thought.

"Do you plant the male kiwi and the female kiwi side by side?" Helen mimed in Castillian.

How else would they do the business?

The CSLWE became animated once again. Rant 3. Like a boxing match. She placed one kiwi in one spot and the other at a chaste distance. I was in favour of accepting that for what it was worth. I felt sure the matter could be Googled were further clarification required.

Helen looked puzzled.

"No comprendo."

Not a bother to the CSLWE. She began by emitting buzzing noises, followed by flapping her wings as in a Basil Fawlty impersonation. The peseta dropped. A bee would visit the male kiwi in his chamber and then fly the missing ingredient (one bag only) to his lady's chamber. Once again, Roberto would be your uncle and, in no time at all, little kiwis.

We thanked profusely the Charming Spanish Lady Without English and, exhausted, left. Helen too. One kiwi each.

The outing had been a good idea. We were both a bit shocked by the previous day's turn of events. Certainly I was and I felt that Helen was too. We weren't a couple who rowed or even disagreed much. And so, where we were was foreign territory, exit strategy not immediately obvious except for the fact that Helen was leaving the following day.

I left her to the airport. We parted in good spirits, all things considered, without further reference to that which was separating us.

"Keep in touch", she said, as she headed into security between the two kiwis. What on earth was that supposed to mean between a couple who had been going out for forty years?

* * *

Once again, Malaga, on my own. This time an unscheduled solitude. I was feeling down. Several hours till the bus back. Only one thing for it. The *tapas* bar and a word with my friend. As ever, packed with suits. No sign of him. I decided to be realistic and ordered a bottle of red. Saving money in the long run.

His painting was still hanging. He hadn't been discovered yet. I looked at it more closely as I sipped my wine and tasted my *tapas*. *Boquerones* and *serrano* ham. I had liked it immediately for its vibrant colours. I liked it even more now. My friend had talent, I thought to myself.

"Amigo", I heard in one ear as I received a slap on the back. "Para ti", he said removing his painting from the wall and handing it to me. "Un regalo."

I was overwhelmed. We embraced as long-losts.

"I cannot", I said.

"*Por qué?*"

"Because, it is too generous."

"*Insisto.*"

"In that case, *muchísimas gracias*", I said and we embraced again.

As best I could, I asked him how the painting was going. He beamed and gave me a thumbs up. Followed by a flapping of his arms which reminded me of the Charming Spanish Lady Without English but I took to mean he was flying. A small modern gallery in a town close to him had adopted him and he was selling a few. He was well pleased.

"*Y tu libro?*" he asked.

"Nearly there", I replied. "Very slow at first and many *distracciónes*. Now it looks as if I might finish it." Partial truth. I finished my report with a reciprocal thumbs up.

"*Estupendo*", Carlos said.

"But, of course, I don't know if it is any good."

"Oh, these *olas negativas*", he said, "negative waves. You English are *incorregible* ...".

"Irish."

"Of course. *Irlandés. Muchísimo siento.* You are so *pesimista.* It must be the weather. Of course it's good. You wouldn't be here if it wasn't." His confidence was just what I needed.

I told him that my wife had come over.

"*Estupendo*", he said. "Not good for *hombre* to be without his woman. Especially a writing *hombre*. We need them around, you know. You will be firing on all cylinders now." His English had improved dramatically since our last meeting.

I told him she had gone back. I had just left her to the *aeropuerto*.

"This not good", he said. "*Por qué?*" he asked.

"*No sé*", I said. "Something about the heat."

"Nonsense", he said. "That's just an excuse." He went off to attend to a lingering suit.

"Maybe you are married too long", he said when he returned. "Time to change your woman", he said matter-of-factly.

"But I love her", I said. I was well into the bottle at this stage. "Do you have a girlfriend?" I asked.

"I do and I love her. For now. But that will change. Everything has its season." The new Spanish man. How long since Franco? "I couldn't survive without a woman but first and foremost it's my art. Same for you. You've come out here to write a book. Go back up there and write it. Find yourself another woman. It's not good for you to be on your own. When you get to the end of the year, reassess. I bet you'll want to stay and keep on writing. Then it's up to her, your woman. She will either come back to you or she won't."

Heady stuff. I wasn't used to such a casual attitude to relationships. Anyway it wasn't as if Helen had said she was leaving me. Simply, that she couldn't hack it here. He was putting a bit of steel back in me. And, of course, as far as the book was concerned he was right. That's why I was here. So get back up there and finish it. Whatever about the finding a woman bit.

"Keep in touch", he said, making more sense than "my woman" a few hours earlier, as I fell off the high stool. Embarrassing. The Spanish don't do falling off high stools.

"Your present", he said.

"Thank you", I said as I put the painting under my arm and the rest of my effort into making as dignified an exit as possible. I slept soundly on the bus back and returned to my empty house in a more determined frame of mind.

That night I had a nightmare. I was hanging by my fingertips from a gutter. I didn't know how I came to be there. Just that I was there. I didn't think I would be able to hang on for much longer. Either the gutter would give way or my tips. I could hear a few people going about their night-time business on the ground below me. I was shouting to them at the top of my voice to get a ladder or, in any event, to do something but of course they couldn't hear me or, if they could, they didn't heed me.

There was a further complication. On the slanted roof tiles just above my head was a rat, a giant hairy rat, to all intents and purposes a monster. Now, I have no hidden agenda when it comes to rats. I don't like them but I am not calling for their extermination. Just on this occasion, this one. Because it was ugly and enormous but, mainly, because it was gnawing at my fingers and sooner rather than later would bring about the separation of fingers and gutter with obvious consequences.

Eventually, I woke. Screaming and in a sweat. Not one for attaching significance to dreams or nightmares, I usually let them go without analysis. Except when I dream that a friend has died in a plane crash. Then I wonder if I should phone him in case he is about to board a plane. But don't because I'm too embarrassed. So, I spend the rest of the day checking the headlines at hourly intervals to make sure that there hasn't been a crash. I was at a low point in my year and I tried to make sense of what I had just been through.

What was the hanging from the gutter all about?

And the people below not hearing me?

And, above all, the rat?

Who or what was THE RAT?

I took the early bus to *Cómpeta* to have a coffee and walk back along The Goat Trail. In an effort to clear my head and unweave my tangled web. *Cómpeta* was only opening its eyes when I arrived and I had the *plaza* and its three restaurants to myself. The sun was inching above the mountain behind the village. It was going to be another beautiful day, though at this moment there was a slight chill in the air and I was sorry I hadn't brought my jumper. A small number of elderly women were emerging from the church where early-morning Mass had just finished. The restaurant staff were putting up the umbrellas and setting their tables in readiness for the day's customers. So cheery, greeting one another, greeting me, greeting villagers and visitors equally. Everyone was *guapa* or *guapo*. It was hard not to respond. And yet my heart was heavy.

I loved everything about the place and frankly didn't know how I was going to settle back to the resumption of my career and life in a city. But that was for another day. For the moment, I couldn't get my head around what Helen had done. She was only here a few weeks and for most of that time her granddaughters were with her. What had got into her? She hadn't given the place a chance. What was wrong with staying and going home once a month for a long weekend? Surely that would have been a good compromise. Instead, an announcement and gone. I was puzzled and cross. I paid my bill and headed for the goat trail. "*Adiós guapo.*"

The goat trail is just that, although I have never seen a goat on it. Walkers and dogs. Occasionally, a runner, a cyclist. Once, a snake. That put me off the place for a while. Bizarrely, two ostriches in an enclosure. Survivors from an ostrich farm.

There are two benches along the trail, one in shade, one not. The elders of the respective villages like to park there, one or the other depending on the season. Sometimes I join them and practise my Spanish, but the chances of my understanding much of their chat are slim. These are mountain men and communication with people who don't speak their language is not their strength. They're not unwilling. On the contrary, they're charming. Just that the ability to make themselves understood by someone who does not share their language is a reserved skill yet to be acquired. And so our conversation is limited. *Hola, buenos días, el tiempo, mucho calor, poco frío, no hablo mucho Español* and the like. Soon enough my novelty value wears off and *los hombres* get on with what they have to talk about. I am left picking up the occasional word that makes it through the language barrier – a source of satisfaction, but nowhere near admitting me to the inner chamber of the conversation.

This morning, I had the two benches to myself. It wasn't yet hot so I chose the bench with light and began my study of lofty *Maroma*. How was I going to get my book finished was my next cerebral port of call? Now that Helen had gone. I had already decided that ruthlessness was key. In this regard, I didn't have an option. If I wanted to finish, that is. How did Helen's departure impact on this?

Not at all if I was to listen to Carlos. What I had to do was clear. From the point of view of us, the ball was in her court. She had pulled out. She could pull in. In default, my task was to complete. Otherwise, the year was a waste of time. I stood up, breathed a sigh of resolution, and resumed the trail.

Back home, I went straight to the white room. *FINISH NOVEL* in capital letters went into the remaining boxes, Rest of September and October. I was fired up. I went to the *ferretería*, hardware store, bought a hammer and a nail and hammered the board into the wall. In the process sending two cracks towards the ceiling so that they looked like aerials coming out of the blackboard. Reg would not be pleased. This would be my flag, my inspiration.

I decided to tidy the room. Nothing like a good tidy. From my barrister days. When the paperwork was getting on top of you, a good clean-out of the torture chamber was yer only man.

In the beginning, there was a bookshelf, empty except for a dictionary, a small table and a chair. You could see the floor. In the meantime, the bookshelf had filled with books, which I suppose wasn't unforeseeable, and the floor had filled with pages. Pages of writing, pages of doodles, biscuit wrappers and sugar sachets with their words of wisdom in Spanish:

Chinese proverb ...

Einstein ...

Marx Karl ...

Marx Groucho ... "*Todo el mundo deberia creer en algo. Creo qué me voy a tomar otro café*" – "Everybody should believe in some-thing. I believe I'm going to have another coffee." ...

I tidied the bookshelf and tidied the floor, meticulously examining each page for a little gem, something that might be of interest to the National Library in years to come.

Everyone in the village knew I was writing a book. I couldn't walk along the *calles*, one of which is named after a home-grown poet, without an enquiry as to whether or not it was finished. There seemed to be a general lack of understanding about how long these things take. I was sorry that I hadn't kept it to myself, at least until the finish was in sight.

In deference to my latest timetable I thought I should inform my buddies. I sent around a text. "Regret. Publisher requires book by Halloween. Out of action until then. *Gracias*." A lie but to the point. I didn't expect anyone to understand. No one ever does. But it might pave the way to a quieter period.

I would disengage. Live like a hermit. *San Anton. Santa Ana.* Wonder if they ever wrote anything. Maybe it was a blessing in disguise, Helen going back. It was only temporary after all and I might finish the book. I would rise early, write until seven and, in view of the fact that I was a failure in the cooking department, eat in one of our restaurants, early and quietly. One glass of wine only. Two on Saturdays. I had always wanted to be a monk. If anyone invited me to join their table, I would decline graciously, muttering something about being *in the zone*. Similarly, if anyone invited me for a drink or to their house. Shouldn't be a problem. No one had so far. I would eat on my own and catch up on my reading. Give *Don Quixote* a rattle. In English of course.

Since I had arrived, I had never seen anyone read a newspaper in the village. Maybe because you couldn't get one. Maybe you couldn't get one because no one read them. With the exception of the beautiful young mum in the *panadería*, I had never seen a Spaniard reading a book. In the village, that is.

END OF MONTH REPORT

Time is running out for Mark. I hadn't anticipated that August would be such a disaster. Not a lot he could have done about it perhaps, but facts are facts. No advance on 25,000 words since end of June and Helen's contribution means that meeting the deadline now seems unlikely.

11

OCTOBER

For the best part of a month, Ben's routine had been the same.

Up late.

Breakfast in the bar between twelve and one.

Black coffee, black toast.

Always the same.

Staring at the ocean.

Sun at his back.

After breakfast, continue staring at the ocean. Sun now making its way around to his left. One or two Spanish in the bar. Not a single Brit. A relief. He couldn't stand tattoos and pints of lager and funny accents. That's why he'd come to the *Costa de la Luz*. Though he was sure it was the Mediterranean. Anyway, the Atlantic wasn't disappointing him.

Around three he would begin to feel peckish. As the tide was turning. No connection. Apart from the getting up late bit, he was keeping Spanish hours. He would summon his favourite *camarera*. There was only one. And order a bottle of white wine. The same one every day. From the north of Spain. He had a wonderful working relationship with the beautiful *camarera*, Aceituna, the Spanish word for Olive. She was warm and welcoming and had a lovely smile. And a very engaging way of closing her eyes for a few seconds at regular intervals during their conversations. Which were entirely one-sided for he hardly spoke.

"*Para comer?*" she would ask at this juncture, knowing his routine. And every day he would reply by pointing behind him to indicate that he wanted the same thing he had had yesterday and the day before yesterday. Namely, *ensalada Costa*. He wasn't adventurous when it came to food and while he spoke fluent Dari, he hadn't a word of Spanish. And that hadn't changed during his first month which was almost up. He tore into his *ensalada* with the confidence that something at least that he was doing was good for him. This was a throwback to his married days. His wife was obsessed with healthy eating. She hardly ate herself and when she did it was nuts and things, but she made sure that he had a healthy diet.

After lunch, he would resume looking at the ocean, which had now gone out. He would continue with his bottle of wine, rarely calling for a second. He drank slowly, which was another good thing and another thing he could thank his wife for. He couldn't come to terms with the divorce so he never referred to her as his ex-wife when he was thanking her. At this point the sun was directly in front of him but he was safe as he was in the shade. Indeed, if at any time he was in the sun, Aceituna would rescue him. Some days he wondered if he might go for a swim until he remembered that he hadn't brought his togs. He never saw the point of the *siesta*, probably because he got up so late.

Around six, he would head up to his room for a shower in anticipation of what the evening might have to offer. Sometimes, he would lie on the bed and stare at the ceiling.

Five past eight on the dot, he would return to the bar where he would order from Aceituna a fillet steak, rare, and a bottle of red. Red was his favourite colour. Red steak, red wine. A *Rioja* or a *Ribero del Duero*. On alternate nights. He wasn't a connoisseur but he knew what he liked. He didn't cover much ground during the day. His room was on the first floor of the adjoining building so he hadn't got far to travel. Two return journeys and, once a day, a walk around the three-sided *plaza* was the height of the exercise. The walk around the *plaza* was another thing he could thank his wife for. She had instilled in him a sense of the importance of exercise. Really, when he thought about it, he had much to be thankful for. By the end of the month, he had put on a little weight and had grown a beard.

Tide back in.

Second bottle of wine.

More staring at the ocean.

Which was difficult to see at this point because it was dark.

Around eleven, Aceituna would escort him as far as his room. Every night. He slept soundly.

Every day the same. The only discordant note was on Aceituna's day off. He didn't like her not being there to look after him and he took it out on the fat owner of the establishment.

Bringing his typewriter down to the bar was the first sign that he was beginning to get his act together. Less time staring at the ocean, another. Drinking less. Well, not drinking more. For all that he was something of a loner, he found his room too lonely. He liked the sound of life going on around him. As long as it stayed around him and didn't intrude. He felt his novel beginning to take shape.

He had enjoyed his eighteen months in Afghanistan. Despite the danger and the difficulties. He managed to get home every six months and he had hoped that his wife might join him there for a holiday but she went to Tenerife instead. His way of dealing with the downside was to throw himself into his work. Criss-crossing the country by train, bus and, occasionally, camel. He worked long hours without as much as a day off in all his time there. At one point he ran himself into the ground and ended up in hospital. First malaria and then dengue fever. Either would have been enough. He attended battle zones and suicide bombings, sending back graphic eye-witness accounts of what he saw. He spent a month living with an Afghan family in the mountains to improve his language skills and get an insight into the local people and their way of life.

He loved the country. Its deserts, its mountains. Its barrenness, its ruggedness. Not unlike what you see on television really. Which shouldn't come as a surprise. He became fascinated by its people, especially its women and their religion. The more covered up the women were, the more fascinated he became. When he was staying with the Afghan family, he became friendly with one of the daughters of the house. Distant friendly. She couldn't be in a room on her own with him. But he could feel her eyes on him. Sometimes their eyes would meet. She didn't wear the burqa in the house but her face was as much as he got to see. On his last night, however it happened, they were on their own together in the sitting room. She hadn't any English. His Dari was coming on but they didn't speak. Just sat there, on either side of the room, staring at one another. By candlelight. No talk. No music. For hours. In silence. Staring. He was good at staring. The following morning he said his goodbyes, never to see her again.

That's what he was going to write about. A western journalist posted to Afghanistan falling in love with an Afghan woman. No mention of lesbian.

Back home on the ranch, the return to work was doing Ben a lot of good. He was coming out of himself. Whatever that means. He was getting up early and, in the bar after breakfast, tapping away with one finger on his typewriter for hours on end. The tide was still coming in and out but he wasn't staring at it as much. When he was, he didn't see it. In his mind's eye, planning the next sentences, totally absorbed. The northern white at lunch was dropped and drinking didn't start until it was dark. It was as if for a month, while drinking his head off, he was writing his book in his head and memorising it and now was the time for transcribing it. There could be little doubt that were Ben to be subjected to professional analysis he would be very close to the spectrum, if not actually on it.

Apart from embarking on his book and drinking less, there was another change in his routine. Instead of just escorting him to his room, Aceituna now went in and stayed the night. Things were looking up for Ben.

Not so for me. At least, not to the same extent. Self-imposed solitude was working. Book motoring. Drinking less. But no Aceituna to escort me to my bedroom. Three out of four, I suppose.

* * *

October. In the context of my most recent timetable, the home straight. A few good weeks behind me. Momentum regained. If I kept this up, I might make it.

Church bells ringing midday. Followed by the doorbell.

"I'm not in", I shouted. It had to be a mate looking for a coffee.

"Oh, yes you are", replied a female voice. How did she know?

"Oh no I'm not." I opened the door.

"Dolores. This is a surprise."

"I hope you don't mind me calling?"

"Of course not. But how did you find me?"

"It's a small village and everyone knows you. I happened to be in the area and thought I'd call in."

"Of course. Come in. Excuse the mess. I've had the head down. No time for light domestics."

"Oh, I've always considered domestics of any kind overrated. Anyway, as I say, I was in the area and thought it would be a chance for me to meet Helen and to invite you over."

"What a lovely invitation. But I'm afraid I'm home alone again." I still hadn't worked out how to explain Helen's departure. I tended to end up giving everyone a different explanation. This time, "She had a medical appointment. You know what these consultants are like. Full of their own importance. You daren't miss an appointment." I was rabbiting on. Too much information.

"The poor thing", said Dolores. She was full of sympathy and, more than likely, insight.

"She'll be fine", I said. Adding irrationally, "But she may need a second appointment of course."

"Not to worry. She'll be back", Dolores said. How Dolores knew she'd be back, I had no idea. And anyway, no one had suggested that she wouldn't be. "Why don't we go for lunch anyway? By the look of things here, you could do with an outing."

"A smashing idea", I said. "I shouldn't of course. I'm hard at it. Deadlines."

"You've got a publisher?"

"Not quite. My own deadline. But I have been working hard and I could do with a break. Where were you thinking of?"

"*El Acebuchal*, Have you heard of it? It's a little gem. Off the beaten track. Not touristy. I wanted to bring you both to it. But let's go ahead. Helen can come another time"

"Sounds wonderful. One condition."

"And what might that be?"

"My treat."

"Let's not worry about the economics."

"No, no. I insist. We go, I pay."

"I'm not going to argue with you."

Half an hour later, we were in the back of her car. Slipping down the Torrox road in the direction of the coast, looking for the turn-off. Apparently there is a back and a front entrance to *El Acebuchal*. We were taking the back. I'm not sure how official it is because there's no sign to point the way. Happily, Jeeves knew where he was going. Or, said he did.

Once we left the main road, we were in a makeshift car parking area but we weren't parking. There were a few exits and Jeeves took one of them. The track was bad and got worse. Surely the wrong one. Narrow, stoney, potholed. I was worried for Dolores's car but Jeeves said it was fine. High suspension. It didn't feel high as we went through the stream at low tide. It was a long ride, very twisty and rising with a sheer drop on my side. I enquired about walking but for some reason that was out of the question. We were going further into the mountains. I'm not mad about heights. In much the same way that I am not mad about needles. So that really I was sorry I had come.

"Lovely drive", I said as we went round yet another bend rather more quickly than I would have liked, causing me to grab tightly what I thought was the armrest between me and Dolores but turned out to be her thigh.

"I'm sorry", I said.

"Not at all", she said.

"Will we be coming back this way", I asked.

"No. There is another road. But this sort of sets the scene. They call it the Lost Village."

I could see why. It's a wonder Franco found it. When we eventually got there, we took a short tour. It didn't take long. It's a small area. I could see immediately that it would be perfect for an artist or, dare I say it, someone trying to write a novel.

"It's been a while", Dolores said, after we ordered. "I meant to get in touch sooner. What have you been up to?"

"Well, August was August. Hot. We survived. Just. Loved *Noche del Vino* and after that it was the *piscina* in the village. September, I suddenly realised that I was running out of time and got down to the writing. And then Helen's appointment came up. For the last few weeks, I've been tied to the desk. I must have it finished by the end of the month."

"How are you finding it?"

"Difficult. You have to be so disciplined. It's not that really. It's that most of my day's work goes in the bin. Writing. Tearing up. Rewriting. Tearing up again. And of course there's the uncertainty. Is it any good? It would be easier if you knew it was good and that it was going to be published."

"Of course it would but not as much fun. Anyway, it is good."

"That's what my friend in Malaga says."

"He's right."

"He hasn't read it."

"Nor have I. But I know you. You've taken a risk. You've come out here. You wouldn't do that unless you knew it was good. Of course you doubt yourself. That's the nature of the beast. Deep down, you know." I was listening intently. Devouring every morsel of encouragement that she might be inclined to drop. "And there's another risk you will have to take." I steeled myself. "You must write full time." I shook my head. "You don't have a choice. You've already made the decision. You didn't come out here to go back. You came out here to go on." She was persuasive.

"And Helen?"

"I can't speak for her."

Between Carlos in Malaga and Dolores in *El Acebuchal*, the going was getting tough.

"May we rest?" I asked.

"Good timing Mark. Here's our meal."

I asked Dolores how she had been. She told me that, since the *Alhambra*, her work for children had brought her to every country in South America. She loves the work, the children – it must have been hard on her not to have had children of her own – and the travelling that goes with it.

After a glorious lunch of venison stew and a bottle of the local red, Antonio el Zumbo, the owner of the restaurant, joined us. It was a quiet day but Dolores told me that even if it wasn't, Antonio, who was something of a missionary in relation to the village, would have found time.

"Would you like to know the history of my village?" he asked.

The tiny village of *Acebuchal* lies in the foothills of the *Tejeda* and *Almijara* National Park. Until 1949 *Acebuchal* was a poor village whose inhabitants produced charcoal and limestone and kept some animals. It was also a resting point for merchants from the coast and nearby towns who were on their way to Granada to sell or exchange their fish, vegetables and fruit which were laden on the backs of mules. This way of life had not changed for two hundred years. No roads. No electricity. No plumbing.

1949. Franco forced the population of *Acebuchal* to move out so that the *Guardia Civil* could move in and use the location as a base to hunt down the guerrillas in the mountains who were continuing to oppose the fascist regime. Over time the village fell into ruin and this was the way it stayed until Antonio, an old resident, took the initiative to renovate the village. The first house was completed in 1998 and after seven years the project was complete. Now, most of the village has been restored but there are still a few ruined houses.

Surprisingly, Antonio gave us this history in English. He explained that he wanted visitors to know first-hand about his village and how it had been treated by Franco, and for this purpose he had gone to the trouble of learning a number of languages. He spoke slowly and with feeling.

When we were leaving, Antonio gave us a present of some home-made bread and some postcards. I promised him I would be back.

I was relieved that Jeeves hadn't turned the car. We took the better track out of the village that had been lost and was found.

"I hope Helen will be better", Dolores said dropping me off, "and don't forget what I said."

Back to my *ermita*. Twenty days to go.

*   *   *

Following morning.

Doorbell.

Who on earth at this hour on a Sunday morning?

At any hour on a Sunday morning?

Hardly the lads not from the gas company.

Possibly the Witnesses. With an interpreter.

I grabbed Helen's dressing gown and flew down the stairs. Why was I bothering? This obsession with answering the door. Let it ring. Just because someone chooses to ring the doorbell is no reason to answer it. I had been having some kind of a low-grade nightmare and sort of panicked. I opened the door. Standing there in Helen's dressing gown that didn't even make it to my knees, I felt undressed. I was undressed. I didn't have my slippers on.

I don't know who I was expecting. I wasn't expecting anyone. That was the point. But once the doorbell rang, the chances were that there would be someone there. And I don't know who I thought it might be. I certainly wasn't expecting who it was.

Madre mía. Of all people. *Nuestra Señora del Rosario.* At that hour. She hadn't called previously. I was taken aback. For the visit, she had put on her posh dress and levitated onto her *trono* and was standing there above me in all my glory. On her own. How did she get there? What was I to do? Had my low-grade nightmare been upgraded to a full-blown vision. Should I invite her in?

At that moment, our friend and neighbour, Lourdes of the *zambomba*, put her head around *Señora*. She had a big grin on her face and was holding out a pretty crocheted bag.

"*Dónde vas?*" Where are you going? She asked. Every time I meet her she asks "*Dónde vas?*" Where on earth did she think I was going? I wasn't going anywhere. It was she who was on the move. I can't work out if the enquiry is intrusive inquisitiveness or meaningless chat.

"What time is it?" I asked. Why I asked it, I don't know. As I asked, the clock chimed midday. "It can't be", I said. "Midday? Heavens." Not much of a soliloquy.

I had now established that Herself was not on her own. I was about to establish that neither was Lourdes. Apart from *Señora*, she had a throng with her and they had just burst into song. She jangled the bag in front of me. I didn't know what this was all about but I had a fair idea I was expected to put something of monetary value in the bag. When your doorbell is rung in the middle of the night and you are confronted by a statue and a choir and a neighbour holding out a pretty bag, it's a fair sign that something like that is expected of you. It's probably universal.

If, say, you had rented a cottage in some remote part of China for your holidays and the doorbell rang on a Sunday morning and when you answered it there was a Buddha sitting on the doorstep and a choir singing and a native holding out a pretty bag, I imagine you would quickly arrive at the conclusion that a donation was called for. Anyway I tore around the house and eventually rustled up a few Euro and put it into the bag.

"*Y Señora?*"

"It's from both of us", I said.

"*Dónde Señora?*"

"Of course." More meaningless chat. Giving her the benefit of the doubt. "In the bed", I said without thinking. "No, in *Irlanda*", I said, contradicting myself.

"*Qué?*" enquired Lourdes. She was right of course. How do you answer that *Señora* is in bed when she's in fact in Ireland?

I explained to Lourdes that I would remove Helen's dressing gown and join her presently. This reassured her and off she went, and her entourage, singing, to the next house.

By now I thought that I knew everything there was to know about processions in the village. And every route. Well I didn't.

The format was familiar. The statue was mounted on a *trono*, a small one this time, and carried by three men and the new mayor, who was breaking new ground. There were villagers to beat the band but, on this occasion, no band.

I fell into line. We followed a specific route and stopped at what seemed to be pre-selected houses. Having said that, some of the houses were empty. In most cases where we stopped, the hall door was open and the man or woman of the house was standing in the doorway. Family photos were arranged just inside the door. The four bearers turned so that the statue faced the people we were calling upon. The bearers transferred the *trono* from their shoulders to four poles, carried separately for the purpose, so they could have a rest. A hymn was sung at each stop. Sometimes there were two or three hall doors very close to one another. No cheapskating. No package deals. A hymn for each open door. When the hymn was finished Lourdes went up to the proprietor for his or her donation which, while the rest of us moved on, was placed discreetly in the pretty bag.

The youngest among us was a fan of *Peppa Pig*. I knew this because he was sporting a hat with the name 'George' on it and I knew from my granddaughters that George is Peppa's younger brother. He was about four and was smartly and warmly togged out with his hat and a matching scarf and loafers, and he was carrying a bag of sweets. He was travelling with his older sister, who if she wasn't careful was going to have her granny's arse long before she wanted it. The oldest among us was another old dear from the church who walked at a right angle using two sticks. How she managed the hills of the village I don't know. Still, no doubt easier than some remote part of China.

We dipped in and out of side streets, sometimes dipping a good bit in and sometimes a good bit out. Even placing *Señora* on the back of a van and whisking her into the *campo* to say *hola*. Some of the people we called to blessed themselves. Some were emotional. Sometimes there was a warm greeting between the person in the house and one of our number, as if they hadn't met for a while. Or, perhaps they meet every day and this is just the warm way in which they greet one another. At one house, the door was open but there was no one in the doorway. Yet the singing started and then a cheery woman from an upstairs window began to shower *Señora* with popcorn from a basin. The connection between popcorn and Our Lady of the Rosary remains a mystery to me.

At about two, we fell into a hangar, half of which was taken up by an enormous truck and the other half by long tables already laid. Time for lunch. *Paella* by Omar, celebrity chef from Buenos Aires, courtesy of the *Ayuntamiento*. We were about fifty. Even so, enough *paella* to feed an army. We sat down and tucked in. Over lunch, I learned that the procession and collection and the day out was to collect money for Christmas in the village.

About four, we got going again. Same routine. Stopping and singing and collecting. Only the fare differed. For the afternoon, it was a shot of everything you wanted and a cake. At every house.

As the clock struck six, we fell into the *plaza*. I wouldn't be needing another *chorizo* or another shot for at least twenty-four hours. A final hymn before the *Ayuntamiento*, the door of which was opened especially by the mayor, who stood in the entrance. You couldn't be singing to a closed door. Up popped Lourdes to the mayor for her donation on behalf of the *Ayuntamiento*.

And then the counting of the money. Done for all to see. And the announcement of the result. Cheers all around. Christmas secure for another year.

* * *

October days were turning. As were the pages of my novel and the colour of the leaves. I was back in the zone and the words were flowing. I was keeping to my programme, eating early, keeping an eye on the *vino* and, with the exception of the trip to the Lost Village, remaining focused. It was now a question of how to end it. The novel.

Ben's pen was flowing too. His Afghan love story unfolding. He was enjoying the opportunity to recall his eighteen months there. The excitement, danger, risk, travel, filing of reports, the difference and, above all, the affair. He threw himself into the affair. His hero was, of course, a married man. It wouldn't be half as interesting if he wasn't. He based their meeting on his last night with his Afghan family, when he and the daughter of the family stayed up the whole night staring at one another. In the fiction, there was a bit more action. It turned out that the daughter of the family wasn't quite as fundamentalist as she ought to have been and, in no time at all, they were tearing into one another. Of course they had to be careful. Allah knows what would have happened to them had they been found out. In that regard a fellow journalist living in a nearby village was extremely accommo-dating. He was away a lot and allowed them to use his comfortable house to 'grow' their relationship. Which was fine until one day out of the red appeared a gentleman engaged by the fellow journalist to redesign the garden. The gentleman in question turned out to be the brother of the not-so-fundamentalist object of our hero's attention.

Ben was happy. Writing by day, Aceituna by night. What would happen when he finished his book? Would he go back to Ireland and the *Irish Times*? Would he stay on and write a sequel? What about Aceituna? Just a passing interest? Would the ending be happy or sad?

Matters were brought to a head one balmy evening. Thursday. As the Atlantic waves rolled in. Aceituna's day off. Ben was eating on his own. In the bar looking out at the ocean, which he was beginning to prefer to the Mediterranean. A good day's writing behind him. He had expanded his dietary habits and was enjoying fresh sea bass. Never a slave to convention, he continued with his red wine even though he was with fish. He had lost weight, was back shaving and altogether was returning to his former self. He was even feeling good about himself.

Out of the blue, as if from the sea, his wife walked in. He hadn't heard from her for months. He hadn't thought of her for months.

"I made a mistake", she said as soon as she sat down.

"In what way?" Ben asked.

"I'm not lesbian after all", she replied.

This is a turn-up for the books, Ben thought to himself. Is this fluidity of sexual orientation or simply indecisiveness?

"And I want you back."

"Where on earth had this come from?", I thought to myself. Denouement threatening.

No sooner had I got the words on the page than the doorbell rang. At ten o'clock at night this was unusual. Unique even. Never Lourdes at that hour and anyway there was no tug on the handle. Dolores knew where I lived now, but while she had form in that she had previously turned up unannounced, I didn't think that ten o'clock at night was her style.

I opened the door.

"Helen", I said, getting the name right. It had been a while. Was this serendipity or what? First Ben's wife, now mine. You couldn't make it up.

"May I come in?" she asked.

"Of course you may. It's your house after all. *Mi casa es tu casa.*"

"I'm sorry", she said. She seemed nervous, which was not like her.

"So am I", I said.

"I should have rung", she said.

"So should I."

"I left."

"Well ...".

"There's something else", she said.

I said nothing.

"I've met someone", she said.

"Of course, you have. You met me forty years ago."

"Someone else. Recently."

I wasn't expecting this. Not like her. She wasn't interested in other men. Not in that way. Not for a moment had it crossed my mind. It wasn't that I was complacent. She was very attractive. I knew that. Wouldn't have married her if she wasn't. At this point no spring chicken perhaps but ageing well. There would have been no shortage of pretenders. Just I never imagined her having an affair or running off with another man. A safe pair of hands as it were. Or so, up to that moment, I had thought. All of a sudden, that assessment, and my marriage, in tatters.

"Is this why you left in September?"

"Yes."

"And why you didn't come out in the first place?"

"I hadn't met him then. I only met him in May. Shortly before my birthday. Do you remember I mentioned a publisher?"

"Of course I do. He wants to publish me."

"That might be exaggerating it a bit. He certainly was happy for you to send it in. Still is."

"That's very nice of him but it won't be happening."

"Of course."

"I don't know what to say."

"There isn't anything. We're adults. We've done well. I've met someone."

"That's a bit clinical. You might be making a big mistake."

"That's a risk I have to take."

"And what about me? Do I not come into it?"

"Of course you do. But you seem happy out here. You're well able to look after yourself. And no doubt you'll meet someone too." She was beginning to sound like Carlos. The dispensable spouse.

"And the forty plus years, what about them?"

"Forty-two to be exact."

"Into recycling? Is that it?" I couldn't believe this was happening.

"No. They were precious years. But things happen. We must move on. We can't cling to the past."

"It's the future I'm clinging to. Finish the book. Christmas here, hopefully with you, then back to the Bar."

"Is that the plan?"

"There wasn't ever any other."

"And now?"

"Well it's a bit early to say. You've only just made your announcement. I'll have to think about it."

"Of course. In the meantime, may I stay the night?"

"Of course. When do you go back?"

"*Mañana*. Midday flight. I'll have to get the early bus"

"That doesn't leave us a lot of time."

"It's probably better that way."

I went for a long walk. Into the mountains. A track I knew well. Full of olive trees and pines and, on this occasion, moonlight. I was having difficulty taking in what Helen had said. She had met someone, she said. Recently. For heaven's sake. We all meet someone. You don't break up your marriage over it. Forty-two years. Happy families. We were close; did everything together. Admittedly my idea of coming out here for a year to write a book had interfered with the rhythm of things. And most of the first six months apart hadn't helped. But I had no idea that under the surface something, perhaps fundamental, was going on. Maybe Helen didn't know either. And then meeting this guy brought things to a head. Maybe if I'd stayed at home. Created spare time to write the book there. Maybe, maybe, maybe.

It was clear from her manner that her mind was made up. She hadn't come over to be pleaded with. Of course I would tell her that I loved her and that I didn't want this but I knew there was no point in arguing with her or in trying to change her mind or beg for time. She wasn't that sort of person. We weren't that sort of couple. She wouldn't have come here with that message unless she had thought it through and was satisfied that it was the only thing to do.

I arrived back at the house exhausted and fell into a deep sleep on the sofa in the sitting room. When I awoke she was gone. She had slipped out quietly, thinking it better not to wake me, she said in her *Dear Mark* letter. It was a nice letter. Nothing like as matter-of-fact as her speech of the night before. It was warm and as comforting as it could be in the circumstances. Listening to her, I had got the impression that I didn't matter to her, that she had outgrown our marriage, which no longer meant anything to her and could be picked up and dropped into the river like a corpse. Not so. She alluded to the very happy times we had had together and apologised profusely for what was now unfolding, which she was unable to do anything about and which was entirely unpremeditated and unsolicited.

By then she would have been at the boarding gate. I texted her. I may have been trying to write a book but I had no idea how to write this text.

"My dearest Helen,

Thank you for your letter.

I am very sad about what is happening but know that you would not take such a step lightly.

I would dearly like to change your mind but I know that your mind is made up.

I wish you well,

M."

After all these years. "I wish you well." Jesus. Is this the best I could do?

First draft. I didn't want to sound angry, though I was. I didn't want to be confrontational. She didn't deserve that. My hands were tied really. My head knew that there was no point in pleading. What was that prayer of Maggie Thatcher (or was it Francis of Assisi?) about changing what could be changed and accepting what couldn't. In the circumstances, I wanted to come across as calm, with some under-standing of the position that she found herself in, even if I didn't have any. I reread what I had written and pressed send.

I had a sick feeling in the pit of my stomach. Something I hadn't experienced for forty years. All those years ago when the girlfriend of the day announced that she was breaking it off. That was the expression we used. Breaking it off. And it marked the end of the world.

Whatever chance Ben's wife had had before Helen's arrival, she had none now. I tore into the book and I tore into her. She couldn't have had any idea of where Ben's vitriol was coming from. A man possessed. He had loved her, given her his best years, he told her, and then this. This business of being lesbian. He had almost said nonsense. She had shattered his life. Wrecked his career into the bargain.

"You can't, my darling", Ben was winding up, his voice filling the empty bar, "play around with people and their emotions like that. After X number of years turn around and say to your partner you're lesbian after all and goodnight and then when you've discovered finally that you're not what you thought you were, turn around and expect to have him back. Life is not like that. You get your turn with the dice and you throw. As my grandmother used to say, you have made your own bed, now lie in it. If you choose to leave your bed for another, there is no way back. Not in my philosophy. Not in anyone's." With that, Ben sat down. He had been standing up. In walked Aceituna, the sun between her thighs. Like a Pilates ball.

In that moment his mind was made up, all outstanding matters resolved. He would ask Aceituna if she would marry him, throw in his job with the *Irish Times* and devote himself to writing. Here on the *Costa de la Luz*. He had been humming and hawing over the past few weeks, wondering where his adventure was leading. And now, in a flash, he knew. And he thanked his wife, who, seeing the writing on the wall, had already left, for making it clear to him.

Ben took Aceituna's hand and led her to the ocean.

"*Te quiero*", he said when they reached the shoreline. "Will you marry me?" he asked. Things were moving quickly.

Aceituna, who had missed the build-up, had no idea what was going on.

"*Qué?*" she managed.

"*Casarse?*" he clarified, not knowing where the word had come from.

"*Casarse?*" she said.

"*Si*", Ben said.

"*Casarse*", she said again. "This is a little, how do you say, out of the blue"; her English coming on. "*Seguro?*" she asked.

"*Si, very seguro*", Ben replied.

"Then so am I", said Aceituna, sealing it.

Aceituna was of the village and loved by everyone. Ben they had taken to themselves. Eventually. At first, he had been alcoholic and aloof. Without knowing why this was so, the locals sensed that he had been through some sort of a trauma and that this wasn't his true self. In time he got himself together and they began to take an interest in him and in his writing. The act of writing rather than what he was writing about, for that remained a mystery to them. His routine fascinated them when he eventually got into one. Coming down earlier and earlier, heading for what had become his corner and passing the day between tapping the typewriter and scribbling away. All the time, filling the floor with rejected manuscript. They had never seen anything like it. The defining turning point in the relationship between

Ben and the locals was when his friendship with Aceituna turned into a full-blown relationship. And now here they were listening to Ben's announcenent of their engagement. Bring on the singers and the clowns. And they did. *Fiesta* was declared. The fat fellow, Aceituna's boss, had joined the gathering at this stage and, quick to pick up the pieces, announced that he would also pick up the tab for the occasion. There was drinking and dancing into the early hours.

Ben's book was coming along nicely and there was no reason to think that he might not finish it sooner rather than later.

As for Ben himself, he had seen off his wife and had decided to settle by the Atlantic with Aceituna and write his heart out. I had Helen to thank for the ending of the story which, up to her arrival, had been eluding me.

Which left me. Not yet the end of October and my book was written. Against all of the odds. My first novel. The first novel ever to come in on time. There on the bookshelf – every typed page of it – for all to read. Who would have put money on it back in May? Was I chuffed? Was I wha'?

My marriage apart, the year out, as an experiment, was looking good. I'm sure no one thought that I would last the year, let alone come up with the goods. "You're very brave", one barrister had said to me. "I've often wondered about doing something like that myself." I knew what that meant. To be frank, I wasn't sure that I would last the pace myself and, certainly, the novel was a shot in the dark, a leap of faith, ranking closer to an aspiration than a commitment. And yet here I was, novel in hand. It had never occurred to me that my marriage could be the casualty.

While the precise moment of putting down the last word was something of an anti-climax – the ending had come a little more abruptly than I had expected – the book's completion called for a celebration.

"*Sergio, gin tónica estupendo, por favour. Una celebración.*"

"*Feliz Cumpleaños, Amigo*", replied Sergio.

"*No, no, no cumpleaños. Mi libro. Terminado.*"

"*Libro, qué libro? Tu no escribes un libro.*"

"*Si. Escribo. Tú sabes. Y terminado.*"

"No, no, Marco. *Tu no escribes un libro. Tu very joking.*" I was puzzled. He was in the frame. I had kept him informed. He hadn't always understood what I was saying but at the very least he knew. He could see that I was puzzled. He whacked me on the back and handed me my gin and tonic.

"My turn for very joking", he said. "*Muchísimas felicitaciones. Eso,* how do you say, *en la casa,* this is in the house."

He was a good man and he had travelled with me. Once more unto the *terraza.* A glorious October evening and I had the terrace to myself, which suited me well. All the more so as Helen wasn't with me. "*Y Señora?*" "No, *Señora* is not with me this evening." "*En casa?*" "*Si. En casa.* She has a headache." An inquisitive lot, the villagers. I was going to have to go public very soon. *Señora* couldn't have a headache every time I went out.

I went back over the months and, in particular, the book's journey. Three pages in three months; June when I wrote the first twenty-five thousand words; September, when, after an unproductive summer, I was in trouble again; and the final outburst when I threw myself into it once more which, paradoxically, mightn't have happened without Helen's intervention. Of course I was thrilled that the book was finished but at the same time I had to handle Helen's leaving. Was there no such thing as joy unbridled? Book, Helen, sundown forever tinged with sadness, Adela on her *terraza* playing the castanets. The whole thing was getting to me and I was nearly in tears. If only she would walk back into my life.

"I thought I might find you here." The Lady from Northern Norway. I stood up immediately and gave Dolores the biggest hug she had had since her husband's passing.

"I'm so glad to see you", I said.

"What's all this about?" she asked, presumably referring to the hug.

"I'm just so glad to see you." And I blurted it all out. The book. Helen. All of a sudden, so lonely, so lonely. She let me talk.

"I'm not surprised", she said when I'd finished. "I knew you'd finish the book and I'm thrilled about that. As for Helen, I can't say anything. I never met her. I'm sorry of course but not surprised."

"Why are you not surprised? I hadn't really spoken of her to you."

"No you hadn't and I can't really say why I'm not surprised but in the short time I've known you she didn't really feature in this great adventure of yours. She wasn't here and then she was and then she was gone again. Instinct I suppose." The sun had dropped out of the picture. As Helen had. And Adela playing the castanets. Sergio kept our glasses ticking over and brought us our evening meal.

Glass by glass I was unwinding. Dolores protecting me from Helen's hurt and we talked about my book.

Around midnight we got the hint. Sergio making noise within. Time to close, the following day his day of rest. He had been there from nine in the morning after all. I was a bit unsteady. Dolores linked me to my hall door.

"Would you like a cup of coffee?" She would. Unfortunately, she had to make it for herself. I had fallen asleep on the sofa. Second time in a month.

* * *

Nine o'clock the next morning.

"I have a publisher." Does she sleep at all?

"Good for you", I said.

"For you", she said. I wasn't functioning yet.

"For me? Wow." Beginning to function.

"He's in London and we have to send it in immediately."

"I'll put it in the post today."

"Email silly. It's the twenty-first century. The post will take a week. He'll have forgotten you by then. Scan it and email it. That way it'll have some chance."

"Scan it?"

"I don't believe this. What sort of a practice did you have anyway?" Eventually we sorted it and off it went.

"It will be ages before you hear from him. If at all." Was it necessary to be that gloomy? "They're notorious. Full of slush piles."

I'd heard of them. Every aspiring author had. The publisher's floor carpeted with unsolicited manuscripts and, more recently, a backlog of email attachments doing the same thing. All the teach-yourself-to-write books said they never got read. And yet, in they came in their thousands. Thousands of wannabe writers defying the odds. Attempting with their covering letter or email to grab the publisher's attention. Who, if they got it, was only going to give the thing two pages, or was it two minutes, before discarding it. At least I might have been given the fast track to rejection.

In the meantime, what was I going to do? It was gone. My reason for being here, over. At last. That which had consumed me for nine months. I still had three left but no Helen. I could read it again. Start the next one. Do an intensive Spanish course. Take up golf.

A week went by.

No news.

Of course not.

There never was going to be.

Not in that short time.

One lives in hope.

The phone rang.

"Is that you Mark?" I recognised the voice but couldn't identify it. Not a great line. "Stan here." Of course, Stan. My number one solicitor. He who had raised my children. Our children. How did I not recognise him immediately? It was only nine months. In practice, hardly a day went by without talking to Stan, at least on the phone. He had been a great supporter over the years.

"I'll cut to the chase. I want you to interrupt whatever it is you are doing out there, God knows, and come back for a case." Signature absence of pleasantries.

"But I'm writing a book Stan, a novel. I told you."

"I'm sure you are Mark but it must be finished by now. Even *War and Peace* got finished." What was this obsession with *War and Peace*? Stan was a solicitor out of the top drawer. Not a creative bone in his body.

"In fact it is. I've just sent it off." An admission. I'd been away too long. Stan was in.

"There you are then. Free as a bird. You'll thank me for this. Just what you need to get you back."

"Let me ...".

"But you've broken up, haven't you?" It was out. How could it not be? "I've spoken to the chair of the Bar Council and the leave of absence isn't a problem." True to form, he had done his homework.

I emailed Dolores to let her know what I was doing.

"Don't let me down", she emailed back.

"One week", I replied. "Two at the most."

END OF MONTH REPORT

You have done it Mark.

Against all the odds. And a few more thrown in.

It is fair to say you have exceeded my expectations.

Congratulations.

I am sorry about Helen but that is outside my area of expertise.

12

NOVEMBER

Dublin was beautiful that November. Crisp mornings, the colour of the leaves and the sun setting on the Liffey at five o'clock. I was so happy in my little village that I hadn't missed it. I certainly hadn't missed traffic and commuting and having to put on a tie. It was strange heading into the Law Library after nine months away.

When I started as a barrister in the seventies, there were only a few of us in the Library. If one of us went missing for even a month it would be a talking point. Forty years on, that was no longer the case. Colleagues simply asked me how I was, as if they hadn't seen me since the previous Friday. A few remarked that they hadn't seen me for a while and moved on. Whatever court calling. With the huge increase in numbers and diversification in work and workplace, one

could be gone for ages and no one would be any the wiser. Stuck in a
tribunal perhaps. Presumed dead.

Stan had me straight into it. Back Sunday. Monday, read the brief,
meet the client. Tuesday, court. I didn't like criminal work and wouldn't
have come back for this case for anyone else. Sex abuse. What else?
Did nothing else go on in Ireland in the twentieth century? What
happened to dancing at the crossroads and sex in the ditch?

This one had an interesting twist. A priest, nothing new, charged
with intercourse with a six-year-old girl in the sixties. Not guilty, my
Lord. On the ground that at the same age he too had been abused,
in his case repeatedly, by a nun in the boarding school which he was
attending. Claiming that the abuse he had suffered in the forties at
the hands of the nun had so deranged him that he could not be held
to be responsible for his rape of the six-year-old girl twenty years
later. Novel. Whatever about the chance of finishing in two weeks it
certainly wasn't going to finish in one.

Nothing had changed in nine months. Judge Grumpy as grumpy
as ever. Prosecuting counsel as tedious. The clock on the wall still
going backwards.

We got stuck in: Stan and I and our junior counsel, who had
her own notions as to how the case should be run. How times had
changed. Not just while I had been away. Things don't move that
quickly in the law. Over a longer period. For twenty years as a junior
counsel, I didn't say a word unless invited to. A new order reigned.

It wasn't my style to identify with my client. I was there to do a job.
To present my client's case to the best of my ability and to undermine
my opponent's. Old school. The job had nothing to do with holding
hands. If the solicitor felt that the client's hand needed holding then
he could do it. Or, ask our junior to, which, in this instance, wouldn't
be necessary as she was already sitting in his lap. Not, in the circumstances, a great plan.

I didn't care whether my client was guilty or not. That was a matter
for him. And the jury. I couldn't know. Guessing was a waste of time.
It was my job to represent him in accordance with his instructions. As
far as I was concerned, having a view as to whether or not he was
guilty was likely to interfere with my conduct of his defence. The same

applied as to whether or not my client was telling the truth. I couldn't know. Judge's job. If I had a view, perhaps a mistaken view, that my client was not telling the truth, then I might not represent him as fully as I ought.

On the Monday, when I was learning the facts of the case for the first time, I was not immediately sympathetic to the defence that I was going to be putting up. Frankly, it seemed like nonsense that you could get out of a sex abuse case on the basis that you had been abused yourself. Indeed, it seemed to be a cowardly sort of defence and I didn't think the jury would buy it.

Here I was at the beginning of what was going to be a lengthy trial with an unlikely defence and an interfering junior. I was missing my *pueblo blanco*.

The prosecution rolled out its case. Nothing too controversial as it happened. After all, we were admitting the rape. On the other hand, the State was strenuously testing our allegation that we had been abused by a nun, since deceased, when we were a child. Not surprising as this allegation hadn't arisen until this prosecution. This was fundamental to our defence, a case within a case. No abuse by nun, no defence. And then there was the evidence, the novel part of the case, as to the effect that abuse had had on us. This was the real nub. Involving psychiatrists and sexologists from all around the country and outside. Was the abuse suffered by the priest as a child the cause of his wrongdoing? In a nutshell. If it was, he gets off. If it wasn't, jail. As simple as that.

The case was causing a stir. It was a groundbreaker in the abuse portfolio. Criminal practitioners were popping their heads into court. It was getting attention in the media. Stan was right. From a personal point of view, it was a very good launching pad for my return to work in the New Year. Indeed, I was beginning to wonder if I should stay on when the case was over. Forget about the last quarter of my gap year. After all, the reason for going had been accomplished. Not for the first time, Stan was looking out for me.

This idea hadn't fully formed in my head when I received a phone call at my desk in the Library at the end of a tough day in court.

"Mr. Barrington?"

"Speaking."

"My name is Ramsbottom ...".

"I beg your pardon?" I had had a long day in court and I was tired.

"I know. It's ridiculous. But it is what it is. I should have got it changed. Please call me Terence."

"Yes Terence. I'm sorry. I'm just out of court."

"Of course. I'm ringing about your book."

My book. Of course. I'd forgotten. Well I hadn't really. But the case had put it to the back of my mind temporarily. Judge Grumpy and all that.

"I've read it."

"You've what? Already? Two pages? Two minutes?"

"All of it. That's what we do when we like something."

I couldn't believe this. I'd had an awful day in court.

"You're not having me on?"

"No. I took the liberty of ringing your mentor, my friend."

"Dolores?"

"Yes. She's a great judge and I place a lot of confidence in her. I told her I liked it. She was very excited and asked me to ring you immediately. By rights of course, I should have rung you first."

"Not at all. I'm delighted you rang her. I can't believe what you're telling me."

"I would like to meet you and I suggest Dolores come along too."

"Whenever you like." This was no time to play hardball.

"The difficulty is this. I am going away at the end of the week – world tour sort of thing, promoting my authors – ...".

... world tour sort of thing, promoting his authors ...

"... and I won't be back until shortly before Christmas which would mean the New Year ...".

"So, you'd like to meet here before the weekend?" I thought I'd shorten things for him.

"Yes. Well London actually. Normally I would come to you – I love Dublin – but because all this has happened rather quickly, thanks to our mutual friend's intervention, I have to ask you to travel to London."

"Of course, that isn't a problem ...", if you leave Grumpy out of the picture, "... I'm in the middle of a trial at the moment but I have an excellent junior or maybe I could come over after court and meet you in the evening?"

"I was going to suggest Friday morning."

"No, you're right, the morning. A much better time. Clearer heads."

"Will we say midday Friday here in my office?"

"Perfect. I'll phone Dolores. See you then Mr. Rams... sorry, bit of a mouthful. Terence." He was gone.

Well, well. What about that. That evening, I phoned Dolores. Two gins later I began to think of Grumpy. Then Stan. Client a poor third. What was I going to do about Friday?

I had heard of an unreported case in the Middle Ages. Something urgent had arisen for one of the senior counsel in the case while it was at hearing. It wasn't a medical thing. By no means a matter of life and death. A domestic matter. Senior counsel needed the following day off to attend to something in his private life. In delivering his decision on the unmeritorious application for an adjournment, the elderly judge recalled that, when he was a student at King's Inns, the Professor of Roman Law had told them that Cicero had once persuaded the Senate to adjourn so that he, Cicero, could honour an appointment with his architect. The judge felt that such a noble precedent could not be ignored and acceded to the application.

I was all set to make my Cicero application on Thursday morning, the day before my clandestine appointment in London with Terence Ramsbottom. However, I didn't have to. When Grumpy sat, he announced that he couldn't sit beyond lunch on that day and was unavailable the next. There was a judges' conference taking place in Copenhagen which the Chief Justice was due to attend. Unfortunately, Chief had taken ill and he, Grumpy, had been asked to step in. What a stroke of luck for the Danes. He apologised profusely to the parties and hoped they understood. Of course they did. What else could they do? It's funny how it's never a problem for his Lordship. Anyway I was off the hook. London later that day. Case to resume Tuesday.

* * *

Dinner that night in London with Dolores, who was as excited as I was though she kept throwing in things like "we're not there yet." To keep me grounded.

As soon as we met at midday in his plush offices overlooking the Thames – I could see the slush pile rising in an ante-room – Terence explained that he only had half an hour before leaving on his world tour. Busy man. I understood. I had to do the same. Not exactly world tours. Other appointments. We call them consultations. I had a heavy enough diary in term.

"In any event, Mark, what I have to say won't take long. And it's all good." There wasn't a mirror in the room but I could feel myself grinning from ear to ear.

We didn't even take the allotted half hour. After about twenty-five minutes we were shaking hands warmly.

"Good luck with your world tour Terry." At this point, I'd completely forgotten his surname and felt that even Terence was too formal, we were so thick.

We were no sooner out of the building than I turned to Dolores and gave her the second biggest hug since her poor husband passed away.

"It's a while since I've eaten here", I lied over late lunch at the Ivy. I wasn't going to let Miss Northern Norway know that it was a first. We went over and over the twenty-five minutes with my new friend. At times Dolores grounding me, at times reassuring. More of the latter.

"You remind me of Woody Allen", she said. "Was it *Hannah and Her Sisters*? The scene where he's just got the all-clear from the doctor. Nothing wrong with him. Nothing at all. Clean bill of health. Jumps for joy. With each step from the doctor's rooms, doubt sets in. Did the doctor say this? Did he say that? When he said this or that, did he mean this or that or something else altogether. And anyway, maybe he missed something. Doctors make mistakes. Look at all those medical negligence actions. Doubled in the last ten years, according to *Time* magazine."

"Woody's right", I said. "It's easy to misinterpret."

"If you want to", Dolores said.

"Maybe he didn't want to disappoint me. Seems a nice sort of chap."

"Mark, you can think whatever you want to think. This guy is a professional. He doesn't go around thinking about people's sensitivities. It's a brutal world. You can take it from me, I was with you. I heard what he said. You're on your way. If you want to be."

I wasn't on my way as easily as that.

"He didn't say he'd publish me."

"Not yet. There's more to be done. This is your first book, your first novel. He likes II. But it can't be published as it stands. Needs revision. Bits to be taken out. Bits to be added. He's giving you an editor. He wouldn't do that, wouldn't waste his time with you, if he didn't like it."

"But my year is nearly up. I gave myself a deadline... ".

"And you've met it."

"Yes, but I'm due back in the Library in January. Stan wants me to stay on after this case. Says I can't be playing around like this. The game is getting more competitive. I've had my fun. Time now to get back down to it or there'll be nothing to get down to. Time moves on; so do solicitors. If that isn't a clear spelling-out from my best solicitor."

"You're right. He's right. Time does move on. But now you have a clear spelling out from your publisher. He wants you to commit for another six months to complete what you've started."

"I don't have six months."

"That's a matter for you. Only you can decide that. Terence couldn't have been more positive. Short of a contract. And that doesn't happen. Now it's time for you to make a big decision. Like you made a year ago. Do I go, do I stay? Only you know."

I was thrilled of course, and, at this point, a little exhausted. Why, just why, couldn't things be more straightforward? Why were there always decisions to be made?

"Now, let's take a break", Dolores said. "Enjoy the moment. You need to sleep on it. Go back to Dublin. Finish your case. Let it tick over in the background. It will resolve itself. In the meantime, I'd like a brandy and what are we going to do for the weekend in this great city?"

I was grateful to Dolores for suggesting that we spend the weekend in London. I should of course have returned to Dublin to spend time with family and friends. But I couldn't face it. Before I left *Canillas* I had contacted Helen to let her know I was coming for the case and that I would like to stay at home rather than in a hotel bedroom. She replied that staying at home wasn't a problem. She and her publisher friend would be in Australia for most of the month visiting his children. So, our house was my house, as it were.

It had been hard enough going back to the empty house every evening to prepare for the next day of the trial. I wasn't keen on doing it for the weekend, so I jumped at Dolores's suggestion.

* * *

"London", I said when Stan asked me on Tuesday morning what I had done for the weekend. "What a city. When a man is tired of London .... It never ceases to excite me. This time it was a business trip."

"I'm glad to hear it Mark. A business trip. You're doing a case over there?" I had been called to the English Bar in the eighties. A fashion at the time.

"Not a case, no. My book."

"I thought you'd got over that", he said.

"Well, this friend of mine in Spain introduced me to this publisher. We sent the manuscript to him and, contrary to all my expectations, he contacted me and said he'd like to meet me. So, we met him in London on Friday before he left on a world tour promoting his authors." Stan wasn't bowled over.

"Friday? We should have been at hearing."

"Lucky break, Grumpy going off"

"And if he hadn't?"

"We'd have made another appointment." Stan wasn't convinced. "Anyway, the upshot is he's interested."

"That's all very well but we're on in a few minutes so we better get back on track." A long weekend in the middle of a trial is always a delight but makes the reality of resumption more difficult.

The team felt we were going well. I never got involved in that sort of day-to-day, witness-to-witness assessment. Wrong too often I suppose. Both ways. Grumpy was hard to read. He was one of the few leftovers from a departing era. A God-fearing Catholic, he would back the Church. That said, he would expect its representatives to live up to their calling and would come down hard on them if they didn't. In this case, its representative hadn't. And I didn't think the ol' fellow would be too taken by the sort of psychiatric babble that we were about to put up to explain why he was not responsible for the rape of the young girl. Thankfully, we had a jury to decide these matters and Grumpy's influence was limited.

As for the jury, for my money there is no point in trying to read a jury. From day to day you'll hear even lawyers say a male jury will think such and such, a female jury such and such else. Rubbish. The jury is a law onto itself and is not controlled by our prejudices. The very point that you might think swings the case conclusively in your favour the jury might not have paid attention to or might not have understood. Nothing for it but to soldier on. Leave the second-guessing to the spectators.

At the rate we were going, we wouldn't finish before the end of the month. And if the judge had to head off to another Christmas market, it could be the New Year. That would be very unsatisfactory for the case and for my conflicting commitments.

I had never had a problem with concentration in the course of my practice. The judge blew the whistle at the start of the case and again at the end. In between I was focused. Not a thing in relation to the case escaped me. Not a thing that was extraneous got through. When I started this case after my nine month layoff, I resumed where I had left off. I had no difficulty giving the case my undivided attention.

When we resumed on the Tuesday, I was having difficulty settling back. The meeting with Terence kept intruding. Follow him? Follow Stan? Carry on; die at my desk in the Library, like hundreds before me? Or listen to that inner voice for once in my life? See if Terence is as good as his word? If he isn't, what's wrong with writing for its own sake? It isn't all about bestsellers.

"Are you alright Mark?" Stan was asking across the bench that divided us.

"Yes, yes. Just wondering about which witness to call next."

It wasn't as if it was twenty years earlier. The children were reared. Helen was gone. There was little to lose. For God's sake, stop beating yourself up. That inner voice.

"Mark."

Jump.

"It's alright Stan. Everything's alright. Talk to you at four."

At four, the whistle went. I told Stan.

"My last case, Stan."

"I was wondering what was going on. I could see you were distracted. Not like you. Always so focused. Well, I'm sorry to hear it and maybe I'll persuade you otherwise but I had a feeling. Your mind hasn't been quite on it these last few days."

That was it. I had made up my mind and had told Stan. There was no way back.

As for the case, I could concentrate on it fully again. We only had a few witnesses left and I decided to leave them to my ambitious junior so that I could concentrate on my closing speech to the jury. I let Stan know what I was doing.

"Are you sure Mark? She's not that long in." You've either been 'around forever' or you're 'not long in'.

"Not a doubt. She's good. Dying to be let out. Not long for junior ranks."

So it was. A few more witnesses. Junior did well. A few more days. Time for closing speeches.

I rose. Gave the best speech of what, on my last day in court, I felt free to call my 'career' at the Bar. I had worked hard on it well into the night. Having regard to the characteristic ponderousness of my opposite number in opening the case, and the likelihood of more of the same when he addressed the jury at the end, I decided, as a matter of tactics, to go for a short, sharp address. They were not going to be put to sleep by me. Having a good memory, I was freed from the necessity of having to refer to notes except for two chunks of evidence which were worth giving in full. I had never rehearsed a speech so often, so, when it came to delivering, it I didn't have to make up what I was going to say next or remember what I had prepared. I was able to concentrate on conviction and conviction they got. Micheál Mac Liammóir may have been a long time dead but he would have been proud of me.

When I sat down, I knew I had done what Stan had brought me home to do. Namely, represent his client to the best of my ability. It was a nice way to go out and I appreciated the note which Stan handed to me from his client: "Whatever the result, I want you to know that I am very happy with how you have represented me." It was generous coming from someone who had so little to win.

I rose and bowed to Grumpy. For the final time. Though he wasn't to know that. The judge addressed the jury last. Traditionally, the junior took the judge's speech to the jury. As I passed her, I whispered in her ear, "Good luck in the Front Bench." I was gone before she could ask how I knew.

I unrobed for the last time and, handing the key of my locker back to the robing master, thanked him for his kindness over the forty-plus years. Within minutes, I was striding down the quays to the Aircoach. On O'Connell Bridge I paused, as I always did at this time of the year, to pay homage to the sun going down the Liffey ... "riverrun, past Eve and Adam's" and, of course, the Four Courts.

It would be too late for the bus when I got into Malaga so I texted Mari-lo, our village taxi-driver, to ask her to collect me. It was lovely to be met with kisses and a big hug. You'd swear I'd been away for a year. On the zigzag road up the mountain in darkness, I texted Dolores. A short text, to the point: "I'm back."

The following day was the first of December.

END OF MONTH REPORT

You ask me, Mark, what I think of your decision.
What I think is this:
You have made your decision. Having made it, your decision is the right one.
May your pen grow wings.

13

CHRISTMAS

Final confession: I have always loved Christmas. Nothing unusual in that. Hard to beat home for Christmas. Hard to beat Grafton Street on Christmas Eve.

It took me a while to get my head around Spanish Christmas. I assumed it would be like home. In particular, that it would be a steady build-up to Christmas Day and Santa Claus. I learned from a Dutch friend here that in the Netherlands they celebrate St Nicholas arriving by boat from Madrid on the fifth of December. By boat from Madrid? Now there's a variation. And when he got there, what did he do between the fifth and the twenty-fifth?

"But that's ridiculous", I said in Spanish. I didn't have Dutch.

"Who are you to say it's ridiculous?" she asked. "You tell your children that Santa Claus heads off from the North Pole every

Christmas Eve on a sleigh pulled by eight reindeer with silly names, criss-crossing the world and leaving a present with every child as he goes. Now, there's ridiculous."

She had a point.

The thing about Christmas in Spain is that it isn't Christmas at all. It's the Three Kings, *Los Tres Reyes*, Caspar, Melchior, Balthazar. We know from our history that they visited Jesus in Bethlehem on the sixth of January, bringing him presents. Indeed that's probably where commercialism began. Bethlehem. They didn't bring one present. They brought three and so Christmas got off to an extravagant start.

"It's not good for the child", María said to José when the lads had left. "He'll be spoilt. Too many presents. It'll get out of hand."

"You're right", said José. "Better nip it in the bud."

Whatever nipping he did didn't work. The thing took off like a house on fire.

The men and women of the *Ayuntamiento* got going with the decorating of the village early in December. Simple fare. Overhead lighting, sparsely hung. Illuminated snowmen. In Andalucía? Illuminated stars. In the *plaza*, the Christmas tree. Bit sparse. Some of the houses had Christmas lights, others a tapestry of the infant. Some had Santa scaling the external wall. Others, the Three *Reyes* climbing a ladder to an upstairs window. Startling enough for the child to have one furry geriatric appear in his bedroom without two more behind. Between this and the crucified Christ outside your window in the middle of the night during *Semana Santa*.

Dolores had replied to my text. She was in Colombia and wouldn't be back in the village until Christmas Eve. She hoped we might spend Christmas together and suggested the *plaza*. Adding that she was delighted with my decision, no doubt in her mind the correct one, and I would not regret it.

So what was I going to do now that I was home alone in the village?

No wife.

No novel.

No career.

The first decision was to do nothing. Absolutely nothing. I was worn out. *Descanso* they call it here. They're always going on about it. *Descanso. Tranquilo.* But I don't think they do half as much of it as they pretend. Well I was going to *descanso*. It had been a stressful few months. Finishing the book, Helen finishing with me, and calling time on my career. I needed to chill. Sleep in in the morning – no adjustment there – siesta in the afternoon and plenty of wine.

When I texted Terence in Japan to tell him of my decision, he replied from San Francisco. World tour alright. He was delighted, he said, and advised me to take things easy and put the book away until the first of January. I could feel his publisher's arm around me. His editor wouldn't be available till then and it would be better for me to come to it with fresh eyes after a break. More *descanso* as it were. We were all on the same page.

Having *descansoed* sufficiently, December was for learning Spanish, chasing ibex in the mountains and getting into the mood for Christmas.

* * *

For starters I needed a haircut.

Up to the top of the village to Montse. We had a good arrangement. She would cut my hair in English. No charge. The villagers were very keen to practise the little English that they had. Or so they said. There was little evidence of it on the ground. Except for Montse and Amable of the *piscina*. Montse had a state-of-the-art salon in the basement of a house. Traditionally where the goats were kept. Until the EU came along and decided that the practice – which had been going on for centuries – offended health and safety and the goats gave way to Montse's *peluqueria*. Opposite the *Ermita* of *Santa Ana*.

The *ermita* or chapel dates from the sixteenth century and is never open. Built by the Moors, it came back to the Christians at the time of the Reconquest, the final event of which was the expulsion of the last Moor from Granada in 1492. According to Ian Gibson, the Reconquest is a misnomer, "the invention of Spanish Roman Catholic historiography."

"I do not know how you can apply the word 'Reconquest' to some-thing lasting for eight centuries", commented the philosopher José Ortega y Gasset in 1921, according to Gibson.

It is said that the Moors had a tunnel leading from the *ermita* to the *campo* to facilitate escape but so far I haven't been able to find it.

Montse has one son, the four-year-old star of the diving pool. According to his mum, Manolo has an enquiring mind. Now Montse wasn't able to express it as clearly as that but we got there. The problem was that now in the run-up to Christmas, he had developed an enquiring anxiety. "How on earth will *Papa Noel*", at that moment busy honing his breaking-and-entering skills on the houses of the *pueblo*, "break and enter into our house as we don't have a *chimenea* (chimney)?" A worthy anxiety for the young hero. No doubt his friends were lurking in the background ready to pounce on Montse's response. There aren't many *chimeneas* in the village. The stakes were high for the young mum.

"In Spain", she began, "*Papa Noel* is not so important." What would the other mums say to her if she got this wrong?. "He is in the nature of a messenger so that not having a *chimenea* doesn't matter. It is the Three Kings who matter. They bring the presents and they come in through the window. All you have to do Manolo is to leave your shoes out, the window open and the Kings will do the rest." So there. Well done Mum. Truth suppressed for another year. And a splendid cut to boot.

On the way out, I asked her about the Moors' tunnel, but she hadn't heard of it.

On account of my writing, I had been unable to devote time to Spanish. Now that that was out of the way and I had made the decision to stay, I was keen to give it my full attention. There were enough of us who, after half a lifetime, hadn't a word of the language. Into the *Ayuntamiento* to enquire. There were a number of levels on offer and, after a stiff on-the-spot examination, the girl behind the desk told me that I was for the beginners' course, which had begun in September. I was already off the pace and she didn't think I would catch up, she told me in near perfect English. She had spent nine months in Terenure as an au pair. Added to which, the rule was that no one could join once the course had started. However, she said she liked the cut of my jib and as numbers were down she would enter me. I immediately stood up and gave her a Spanish kiss, which is of course quite different from a French one.

Apparently, Maestra was having a baby so there would be no class that week. She wasn't having the baby till June but sometimes her Spanish class clashed with her pre-natal. Only one class left before Christmas and, in the ordinary way, she would ask me not to turn up until January. However, as the last class would in fact be the Christmas party, it would be an ideal opportunity for me to meet everyone.

When I was at school, our foreign languages were Latin, French and Irish. One lad in the class was learning Russian. He wanted to be a spy. James Bond and Ursula Andress had just come on the scene. Where would I speak Latin? The priesthood, possibly. Or, for that matter, Irish?

As for a living language, with all the help we had received from the Peninsula down the years – the Spanish Armada, au pairs from Madrid – why hadn't the Department of Education anticipated the Irish obsession with Spain as a holiday destination? In which event, the Saints and Scholars might do better than "*Viva España*" when ordering a drink on the *Costa del Olé*.

French is all very well, but they won't speak it to you. Whoever stopped a Parisian on the *Champs-Élysées* to ask the way to *Stade de France* in French? Waste of time. May as well be talking to a North Korean. Or someone from the House of Lords. He'll pretend he hasn't a clue what you're saying in that self-effacing Gaullist way and reply in annoyingly good English. And they always seem to be taller than you. Must have something to do with de Gaulle's nose.

So here I was at ten in the morning a few days before Christmas, ready to immerse myself in the Spanish language. At about a quarter to eleven the class arrived. Mixture of us and them. I wasn't expecting them, except for Maestra of course. They were there to read and write. They had been left out in Franco's time.

Maestra welcomed me warmly and announced that while this was *fiesta*, we would *fiesta* in Spanish. It was hard going, as the racing pundits put it. I didn't understand a word the Spaniards said. It was difficult enough to understand the English. I feared that this beginners' class was too advanced for me. In both languages.

No one had told me that the people in the south of Spain, and in particular the people of the mountains in the south of Spain, speak a different language. Called Andaluz. I knew of Basque. I knew of Catalan. Couldn't speak them of course. But Andaluz? Hadn't even heard of it. Even Spaniards from outside the region have difficulty with it.

They drop the 's' for a start. 'Buenos días' becomes 'bueno día'. On its own, not insurmountable. They drop most of each word they utter so that words run into one another. They speak faster than anyone else on the planet, with the possible exception of anyone from Cork. You really don't have a chance. All you're left with is gesticulation. And repetition of a few hardy annuals: si ... gracias ... bueno ... mucho sol ... qué calor ... vamos ... venga .... The party hadn't begun and I was exhausted.

I wasn't sure what meal we'd been invited for. There weren't any cornflakes. Grated tomato on toast. Local oil. Pan. Garlic to beat the band. A range of chorizo and cheese. A frightful thing called bacalao, slices of dried, salted cod. Inedible. I mistook it for manchego and had no option but to spit it out. On my first day. A few shots of the local vino dulce by way of anaesthetic. It wasn't all about the food. It was an opportunity to get to know one another and speak Spanish.

Just as well that Maestra had another party to go to. Or we'd still be there. With her charm and a sprinkling of olé, olé, olé soaked in anís, international barriers were torn down. Like the statues of dictators during a coup. Toppled. Sundered. We were talking in tongues. Andalucía was the finest place in the world in which to live and Canillas would host the next World Cup. On that note we broke up, promising to meet again in a year's time. If not before. January maybe.

I was looking forward to Dolores's return. It was lonely without Helen. Admittedly, there was anger mixed with loneliness, but the latter won out. Who fares best in these situations, I wondered by night, alone. The man? The woman? What do the experts say? There must be plenty of reports. About ten the night before Christmas Eve, the landline rang. It hadn't rung before.

"Mark?"

"Helen?" This was a surprise. "I was just thinking of you." Well I had been. "How are you?" A bit too keen maybe.

"I'm fine thank you. Just fine." She sounded hesitant.

"Happy Christmas", I said. I didn't want any argy-bargy. While I didn't like the situation I was in I was coping reasonably well. I didn't want to rock the boat. My boat. Hers was probably fine.

In the seconds between exchanges, everything went through my mind. Her departure in September. Her twelve-hour visit in October to make full disclosure. Why was she ringing now? At ten o'clock, the night before Christmas Eve? The phone was so unsatisfactory. To say that she had made a dreadful mistake perhaps? She had realised very quickly but was too embarrassed to get in touch. She was so dreadfully sorry and would I have her back.

"I want a divorce." Well that put paid to that. I was stunned. Once again something that had never entered my head. I was speechless. It certainly wasn't festive fare. She wasn't saying anything so eventually I pulled myself together.

"I like your timing Helen."

"There's no need to be smart Mark. This is a serious matter. It isn't easy making this phone call." As if, for one moment, I cared how not easy it was for her to phone. Anger rising.

"Helen, it's ten o'clock at night, the night before Christmas Eve. You walked out and you phone me now to tell me you want a divorce."

"In summary, yes. There isn't any other way to say it."

"Well, there isn't any other way to say this either. You can stuff your divorce. Now, I'm putting the phone down. Good night." And I did. For the first time ever on anyone. Probably not a good idea. I would regret it in the morning. For the moment, it gave me a good feeling.

A few minutes later, it rang again and rang and rang.

The following morning, I was still furious. To be fair, that wasn't the Helen I had lived with for forty years. But I was in no mood to be fair. She could talk to her lawyers, as they say in the movies. I knew then, if I hadn't known before. She wasn't coming back. Her phone call had done me a favour. Since she left I had clung to the hope that we might get back together somehow. That everything would be sorted and we would resume our adventure here. Suddenly, I knew that was gone. Irretrievably. Somehow, it made everything easier.

Dolores had broken her journey from Colombia with two nights in Madrid. She couldn't be within thirty-five thousand feet of a capital city without dropping in. Friends everywhere. She arrived refreshed at midday on the dot after a two-and-a-half-hour journey from the capital by the bullet train, *AVE*. It was wonderful to see her, particularly after the night before. I gave her a great big welcome and promised her a lovely Christmas.

Beginning with our first engagement, for which we were already late. Carol singing in *Cómpeta*. The Spanish don't do carol singing, so I hadn't had carol singers at the door singing 'Good King Wenceslas looked out' in bright sunshine until I asked them to move on. What we were going to was an ad hoc gathering of a few ex-pats who couldn't necessarily sing but were well-intentioned and shared the belief that Christmas wasn't Christmas without 'Jingle Bells'. Just as well we were ex-patting in Spain and not Afghanistan.

We needn't have worried about being late. *Plaza de la Constitución*, our meeting place, was practically empty. The only sign of a carol was Fred in a Santa hat sitting at the bar, warming up his vocals with a few beers. At least it was only Fred who was having the beers. He was the one with the voice. He had been in a choir. In the past. So long as his vocals didn't get drowned. Over the next half-hour another handful arrived so that at four o'clock we could declare the ad hoc gathering gathered. Time for leadership and rehearsal. Fred, despite his hat, assumed leadership. And attempted rehearsal.

"An easy one to begin with: 'Hark the Herald Angels Sing'." Fred stuck his tuning fork in his ear and off we went.

"Stop", he roared before we had gone very far. "That's awful."

"What do you expect when we've never sung before?" My friend Daisy had her own leadership ambitions.

"Do you think that singing beforehand would have made the slightest difference?" Fred wasn't for lying down.

"We'll nay know now", said Daisy, who was from Scotland and had been to *La Scala*.

"Oh come on", said Lizzy, a peacemaker from Newcastle with a pacemaker. "Tis the season of goodwill after all."

"Yes, come on", we all declared, staring at Fred and Daisy.

"All for one and one for all", said Luke, getting his occasions mixed up. Fred and Daisy silently agreed on a joint leadership programme and hugged. Once more unto the *plaza*.

The few people who had been there had gone. We didn't take their departure personally because we didn't know that they knew we were coming. And anyway, it had begun to rain. Christmas Eve in *Plaza de la Constitución*. It wasn't Grafton Street. There was a marked absence of hustle and bustle and last-minute shoppers laden with presents running in and out of Brown Thomas. No one could say that Christmas had gone to *Cómpeta's* head.

The absence of an audience wasn't going to deter us. We weren't going to let all that assembling go to waste. Fred raised his tuning fork to Daisy's ear this time and we sang 'Away in a Manger' beautifully to an empty *plaza*, receiving a standing ovation and a complimentary shot from José for our trouble. He didn't ask for an encore but he got one. 'Twelve Days of Christmas'. Day eight and as many maids a-milking and he had to lock up. We moved on.

During the afternoon we brought cheer to many an empty establishment. Our repertoire of carols was limited so we improvised. By the end of the afternoon, it included a heartfelt rendition of 'Flower of Scotland' and 'Take Her Up to Monto', a moving tribute to a red-light district in Dublin at the turn of the century. The previous century.

By six o'clock – at a shot a carol on the respective establishments we visited – probably to get rid of us – who was to spot that these weren't timeless seasonal songs from the homeland?

At seven, we were back in *Canillas*. Rodriguez dressed up as Santa Claus and went around the village on his motorbike ringing his bell with gusto, calling the children of the village to decorate the Christmas tree.

At nine, the bells rang out for Midnight Mass.

The church choir surpassed itself. As did Rodriguez, tree done. Popping in and out of the church in his red vestments, keeping an eye on his soul and his customers, some of whom had abandoned their tables for Mass. They weren't intending to but when they found it on their doorstep. People get sentimental at Christmas. I was expecting Rodriguez to come in and take their orders.

At eleven, Dolores and I joined him and his family for Christmas dinner.

* * *

Día de Navidad

I have always admired those who are prepared to make sacrifices. For their sport, their god, their art, their whatever. I am an admirer of other people's sacrifices.

For example:

Athletes driving their bodies through the limit in pursuit of excellence. I was too young for our own Ronnie Delany in Melbourne in 1956. I was ten when Herb Elliott won the 1,500 metres in the Rome Olympics in 1960. I remember every metre of it. Training at home in Australia, he ran up and down sand dunes until he was sick.

Monks in their monasteries in the south of France showering in mountain water in the depths of winter.[†]

Closer to home, those who swim on Christmas day. Half of Dublin descends on the Forty Foot – a bathing place without frills a few miles south of the city centre. Just around the corner from the tower where Joyce and St John Gogarty stayed briefly in 1909 and forever more in *Ulysses*. No matter how many degrees below zero, a party prevails: Buskers, people collecting for charity, hot toddies, good humour, laughter, Happy Christmas.

Hardy souls stripping
towels slipping
breasts beating
chests
caps adjusting
queuing

[†] As portrayed in the film *Into Great Silence*, a film by Philip Gröning.

to dive or –
at the last moment
a change of mind –
jump in
envying those done and dusted
dressed.
Queuing for the rusty ladder
to the sea below
cautious descent
no time at the bottom
to test the water
in the name of the Father
this could be the last time
may be the last time
the screams of the condemned
beyond
the point of return
as each body hits the
water
reality
a few strokes
no more
none fatal
out
done
till next Madness Day.
"Not as bad as I expected", one swimmer to another.
"Better than last year", the other, who keeps records.
A towel and a warm word from a family member. Home.
No matter how many times I say "I don't", I do. I do mind. Ever
an onlooker, I want to be one of those swimmers in the Forty Foot on
Christmas Day who
turn up
expose their bodies
to wind and rain
the grey

and that moment of truth
like those monks in the south of France
like Herb Eliott
and Ronnie Delany.

Not even this year, when it was the Mediterranean and not the Forty Foot, would I endanger my immortal cowardice. Dolores swam alone.

The Christmas Day auction, scheduled to start at eight, started at eight. Taking me by surprise. The new mayor – perhaps standing for a new order – was standing on a table in the *plaza* taking bids. The Christmas tree towered over her. It was dark and cold. A more likely explanation for the punctuality. She was doing a good job and, if not re-elected, had just added another career option to her bow. Holding up a bottle of whiskey in one hand and a live rabbit in the other, the bids came in fast and furious. The auction was financing the presents for the children of the village from the Three Kings. It was promising to be a bumper year for them. The whiskey and rabbit were knocked down to my elderly friend who goes to Mass every Sunday, who was herself knocked down by the rabbit on her way home.

The mayor seemed to be trying to achieve a balance between a bottle in one hand and a live animal in the other. On one occasion the bottle was withdrawn, as the main item for auction was a sheep wrapped around her neck like a fur collar, needing both hands. The bidding took off, as did the sheep at the first opportunity. Unfortunately for the sheep, while it's in a league of its own on mountain paths, it's not great in crowds, with the result that its bid for freedom was quickly foiled and it was returned to the mayor's neck. Bidding continued while this diversion was playing out. I don't know where the bank manager's wife was during the sheep's escape, but the price she paid for it, and the expression on her face when it was handed down to her, suggested that she thought that what was wrapped around the mayor's neck was a fur collar and not Sunday's roast. This lot alone would cover a sackful of presents.

At the end of the evening, the proceeds and two leftover chickens were handed over to the Three Kings, who were standing by. Such was the success of the auction that the children's chances of receiving what they had asked for from the royals had surely been enhanced, along with the new mayor's chances of re-election. The Kings were delighted too. This year wouldn't cost them as much as the previous one. It hadn't been a good year for oil after all.

The *plaza* emptied; the restaurant filled. Boom time for Rodriguez. He was very good. He never drank on the job. The auction was an exception and a welcome one at that, because his merry generosity boosted the budget for the presents.

Back in Dolores's palace, back on the *Carlos Primero*, I was telling her about Helen's phone call. The Carlos was going down very well, along with everything else I had had to drink during the auction. I wasn't pulling my punches. I let Dolores know in no uncertain terms what exactly I thought of my wife and her phone call. I was probably piling it on a bit in the certainty that, knowing Dolores, she would restore some balance to my rant and point out the stress Helen was undoubtedly under. The sisterhood and all that.

"She did WHAT?" Dolores said. I had just told her. When I repeated it, she added, "THE BITCH."

Then we went over it again.

"She phoned you the night before Christmas Eve?"

"Yes."

"Ten o'clock?" I didn't think the time was all that important. It could have been nine.

"Yes."

"She had walked out on you back in October?"

"Yes."

"And now SHE was looking for a divorce?" I thought that all of these facts were well and truly established.

"The night before Christmas Eve?"

"Yes."

"At nine o'clock?"

"Ten."

One thing I was pleased about was the way Dolores was picking up on the very points that I had made to Helen in the course of our telephone conversation forty-eight hours previously. I was too close to the problem and might highlight the wrong points. Not so. Dolores, an independent listener, was in total agreement.

"THE BITCH", she said again.

I didn't want to agree with Dolores on this. At the end of the day, Helen was my wife and I loved her; Dolores an outsider. Foreign countries and all that. BITCH was strong.

"I can't disagree with you", I heard myself say. Dolores was right. Helen was a BITCH.

On that note of narrowing the gap between agreement and disagreement we went to bed.

The following morning, Dolores was contrite.

"I spoke out of turn last night Mark", she said over a light meal that was neither breakfast nor lunch. "It's none of my business."

"I made it your business. I bored you to death with my domestic matters in the middle of a lovely Christmas. I'm the one who should be apologising. Let's call it quits and go back to bed." Stephen's Day was never much of a day anyway. With or without the wren.

14

NEW YEAR'S EVE II

I was really looking forward to Danny and Kate's visit for New Year. A promise made at Faro airport a year earlier.

"See you in your *pueblo blanco* in a year's time." Danny's parting words to me as he boarded. "We can have a public reading. Booker Prize here we come", he mocked.

"You might be surprised", I replied, waving them off.

Truth be told, I was the only one of the four who thought there would be a novel at the end of the year. The one thing that no one anticipated was that there wouldn't be a marriage. We had been a solid couple and, were anyone putting money on it – not appropriate I suppose – it would have been that we would see it through. But life doesn't always deliver in accordance with expectation. The favourite doesn't always win.

"You don't have to come Danny. Things have changed. I know that. Goal posts moved. Kate might be uncomfortable." I had phoned Danny earlier in the month, not to tell him about us – he would have known about that early on, Helen and Kate were very close. Of course they couldn't come and I wanted to make it as easy as possible for them.

"You can't put us off that easily. We are certainly coming. Helen's loss. Kate thinks she has lost the plot. At her age and all that." You could have bowled me over. Another delivery not in accordance with expectation. I told him so. He had been such a supporter of the book. And now this.

"You've made my Christmas Danny."

"I'll read it while I'm there. No big words I hope. See you on the 30th. Same Christmas present as last year please."

I wasn't sure what to do about accommodation. The house was too small for the three of us. It wasn't like their place in Portugal. Anyway, I couldn't stand people staying. Dolores to the rescue.

"Why don't you stay here and let them have the house?" Perfect.

They arrived late on the 30th, so we didn't really get going until the pageant in the *plaza* on New Year's Eve.

For much of the time, most of the year, our *plaza* is empty. Compared to the signature *plazas* of Spain, ours is a miniature. Only a few people live in it. Only a few more pass through. When Malaga plays Barcelona, the wall of the church becomes a goal; in summer, a screen for outdoor cinema. When the sun is shining, there may be a few people having a coffee or a drink during the day and, from June to October, the restaurant moves outdoors. Footfall won't bother the environmentalists.

Most of the time, all that can be heard is the fountain and the church bells every fifteen minutes. The bells get excited announcing Sunday Mass. As for a wedding. When someone of the village dies, they toll. Occasionally, a child calling "*Abuela*" to open the door. After dark during the warm months, a grandee of the village takes his accordion to the bench alongside the goal wall of the church.

On New Year's Eve, not only was the *plaza* busy, it was transformed. In a matter of hours it had been converted into a number of

Middle-Eastern villages at the time of Herod. When darkness fell at six o'clock, all we had for lighting was the fires on which Middle-Eastern villagers were cooking *patatas a lo pobre* and popcorn. It was the first time since I had come to Spain that *paella* wasn't on the menu. From which I inferred that *paella* wasn't a dish they went in for in the Middle East. Whatever about popcorn.

Mária went into José in his workshop – he was making a bookshelf at the time – to tell him that, while she was preparing the lunch, an angel had called to tell her that she was going to have a baby. Mária, not the angel. How the angel knew was what is called a mystery, not a miracle. This came as a surprise to José, who was engrossed in his work. And indeed to Mária. José responded by putting Mária on a donkey. With some difficulty. She is a big girl. Eventually they got it together and off they went in some direction. After a while, the donkey got tired and refused to go any further. Whereupon José, who appeared to wear the trousers in the relationship, asked innkeeper Rodriguez, whom he didn't know from Adam, if they could stay in his inn. Rodriguez said no, they couldn't. He didn't give a reason. Under the law of whatever land they were in at the time, if an innkeeper refused you a room, he had to give you a reason. Not a room, just a reason. Whereupon José, who may only have been a humble carpenter but was well up on these things, asked for one.

"We're full", Rodriguez said in the language of the people who live between Nazareth and Bethlehem. "It's the Winter Olympics."

"No, it's not", said a bureaucrat from Brussels who knew the language in question. "They're not until next week. You've plenty of rooms."

"You keep out of this", said Rodriguez, "it's none of your business." Whereupon José, a vegetarian, picked up Mária and carried on to Bethlehem, leaving the donkey behind. *Qué hombre.*

There was no problem with accommodation in Bethlehem and they were quickly shown to a superior stable. They were keen to get a stable with a view on account of the imminence of the new arrival. This puzzled the new innkeeper, who bore a close resemblance to innkeeper Rodriguez, because he couldn't see what the new arrival would be doing with a view. José explained to the puzzled innkeeper that the new arrival was the Son of God, to which the innkeeper responded that he didn't care who he was the son of and anyway a stable with a view wasn't possible as all the stables were inward looking.

They weren't leaving until the sixth of January as they were expecting visitors from the East. This of course meant additional expense for the young couple as they had been told by the gynaecologist that the baby would come early, like the English. When they were leaving, they asked for the Book of Comments wherein they suggested building some stables with a view and installing Wi-Fi. Ending, on a positive note, that they looked forward to staying there again on their next visit to Bethlehem.

The baby arrived on Christmas Day. Which was a great relief to the world economy. Imagine if it hadn't. Imagine if it had arrived on … say … the second of January. Not just another day, another year. But, another celebration. More time off work. Offices and factories closed. How on earth would we pay the bills?

José insisted on being present at the birth. There was no one else around, being the holiday period. He thereby started a trend which didn't take off for another 2,000 years. What is called a slow burner. It was good of José, particularly as there was a question mark (?) over paternity.

By New Year, José and Mária were keen to go and, anyway, they had run out of conversation. But they couldn't. They had promised their friends from the East. They didn't know where in the East they were coming from, so they couldn't contact them to make an alternative arrangement. Early on the sixth, the friends arrived, full of the joys of East. They had a lovely day together, though for some reason Balthazar stayed on his camel throughout the visit. When the friends found out that they were without donkey, they insisted on giving them Balthazar's camel. They held on to Balthazar. The difficulty which Mária had had mounting the donkey was nothing to the difficulty she had mounting the camel. At dawn the next morning or, maybe, it was first light, José and Mária headed off on camelback. Unfortunately, they forgot the baby and had to go back. Eventually, around eleven, they were on their way again. Only, an hour later at the only crossroads for miles, to encounter a shady-looking character standing a foot clear of the dusty road and holding a sign which said that Jerusalem was closed for the day as it was Herod's birthday and to take the road less travelled. This diversion added two days at least to the journey home but in all likelihood saved their lives. No matter, or as the Spanish say *no pasa nada*. They were in no hurry.

In this way, the busy story of the birth of Jesus was handed down from one generation of *Canillero* to another. In view of the number of people watching the journey from their balconies, it would appear that innkeeper Rodriguez was telling the truth when he said his inn was full and is entitled to an apology from the Brussels bureaucrat, which he is pursuing through the appropriate channels.

Danny and Kate were delighted with all of this. All of which was new to them. Not the story, they were churchgoers. The setting. They had no experience of village life and probably didn't want any. The Algarve was as far north in Portugal as they had been. They hadn't seen an Irish village let alone a Middle-Eastern one. And as for a camel, the cigarette was as near as they would have got. But they were taking it in their stride, *hola*ing everyone like true tourists. I was thrilled to be showing them my village.

A year to the day, we had been on the patio of their splendid villa listening to fireworks and crickets as I told them about our plan. They had thrown themselves into our adventure then as they were throwing themselves into their adventure now. Three nights here and then driving across Spain to continue their New Year holiday.

"We're so sorry about you and Helen", said Danny. Pageant over for another year. We were on our roof terrace and Danny was smoking this year's Christmas present. It was a golden evening full of stars and mountain. Dolores had disappeared to get more gin.

"Thanks." What else could I say?

"We were completely taken aback. Of all couples."

"Me too. It had never entered my head. I am so grateful to you for coming out. It's great to see you both. Thank you, Kate, for coming."

"Our pleasure", said Kate. "Danny has been talking about it all year."

The crickets had started up. There were no fireworks. Dolores was back with the gin.

"So you've got it finished?" said Danny puffing. I felt he was more relaxed than before.

"It wasn't easy. I'd never have taken it on had I known it was going to be so difficult and so time-consuming."

"And you've a publisher?"

"Yes. Nothing in stone. He's giving me an editor and another six months and will make the final decision then."

"Yes, but he wouldn't be doing that if he wasn't serious. He'll take you on alright", chipped in Dolores.

"Friend of Dolores", I said.

"Not relevant. Those days are over. Everything is about money now. He wouldn't be doing this if he didn't think you were commercially viable."

"I have to agree with Dolores there. It's all about money", said Danny. "I can say it now. I thought you were mad when you told us. Heading off for a year", said Danny.

"You said it then."

"But you were also a bit jealous", said Kate.

"True. Not the writing bit. The year out, life in a village."

"You in a village Danny? It would have to be a designer village. With a golf course."

"Who told you about *pueblos blancos*?" I had forgotten.

"Talking about your practice, darling" – no one mentioned my practice – "you never told me the result of your case. Your last case."

"What's that all about?" asked Kate.

"At the end of October I got a phone call from my best solicitor. He wanted me to come back for a case. Special case. A favour, sort of. It so happened Helen had just left and I had just finished the book. I was at a bit of a loose end and of course Stan is very persuasive, so I agreed. It was listed for a week. Went on for four. It was during it that I realised it was over. My time as a barrister. Time to hang up the briefs. I was getting stale. I gave my last case my best shot. When closing speeches come to be talked about …".

"And, what happened? How did your last case go?" asked Kate.

"I don't know."

"You don't know? You must know. You were there."

"Not at the end. When I finished my last address to a jury, I left court. I left my junior to handle the rest and anyway she's about to take silk. I unrobed, returned my key to the robing master and walked out of the Four Courts for the last time."

"Not a bad exit", said Dolores. "As Jerry Hall said, it's all about the exit."

"But the result?" asked Kate. "You must know if your client got off or not? After all that work on his behalf. Your last case. Are you not consumed with curiosity? I know I would be."

"I asked Stan not to tell me."

"Why?"

"I don't know. I just didn't want to know the result. I had given it all I had. The result was outside my control. Were he acquitted I would be delighted. Convicted, disappointed. But really that was none of my business. My business was to do my best to get him acquitted. I had done my best."

"Your last case and you'll never know how it ended?" said Kate.

"Exactly. I haven't thought about it since I walked out of the Four Courts."

"And your book Mark. Is it the same with that?" asked Dolores. "Write the best you can, produce the best book you can and whether it gets published or not, whether it sells or not is immaterial?"

"I hadn't thought of that. But I suppose you're right. All you can do is give it your best shot."

"You mean you don't care whether it's published or not, whether it sells or not?" Danny knew me alright.

"No Danny, I'm not saying that."

"Well, if it's any encouragement, I'm halfway through and enjoying it enormously. Now, it's five to midnight. What happens in Spain?"

"Be upstanding", said Dolores as she poured the cava and distributed the grapes. Twelve to each. One at a chime. The grapes of midnight. The twelve months of the old, the twelve of the new. The bells chimed. The crickets went up a notch. The fireworks crackled. Grapes and kisses. What a year it had been. What on earth to come?

As we went home in Dolores's car, I checked my phone.

Three missed calls.

One from New York.

Now that I'm older, losing my hair ...

GLOSSARY

... of Spanish and Irish words for the benefit of readers not familiar with these languages.

abajo, abajo	down the hatch
arriba, arriba	up, up
arroyo	stream
Ayuntamiento	Town Hall
buenas tardes	good afternoon
cailín	*chica*
calle	street
camarera	waitress
camino	way
campo	you either live in the pueblo or the campo
Canillero	someone from *Canillas*
casa	house, home
cementerio	cemetery
chica	girl
chupito	a shot on the house
comida	meal

conas atá tú? Tá mé go maith, go raibh maith agat	how are you? I am very well, thank you
conquistador	a conqueror back from South America
cúpla focal	the few words (in Irish)
Dama de Noche	a flower with a beautiful scent which you only get at night, called Lady of the Night, cestrum nocturnum
descanso	rest
deus ex machina	neither Spanish nor Irish, look it up yourself
Domingo de Ramos	Palm Sunday (ramos means branches)
dónde mi amigo?	where is my friend?
dónde vas?	where are you going?
encantado	delighted
ermita	chapel
Feliz Cumpleaños	Happy Birthday
guapo, guapa	handsome, pretty, gorgeous
huevo	egg
no fumar	no smoking
no pasa nada	not a bother
panadería	bread shop
para comer?	what would you like to eat?
paseo	short walk, stroll, very much a Spanish thing when the intense heat goes out of the day
patatas a lo pobre	poor man's potatoes
peligroso	dangerous
pisadores	the fellows who tread the grapes
posada	inn
postre	dessert
pueblo blanco	white village, a feature of Andalucía
qué hombre	what a man
qué pasa?	what's up? what's happening?
qué tal?	howya?
regalo	present
rodilla	knee

Semana Santa	Holy Week
sierras	mountains
sin nata	without cream
sláinte	cheers, *salud*
trabaja mañana	work tomorrow
trono	throne, the platform on which the statues are placed and which is then carried on the men's shoulders during *Semana Santa* processions
vamos	let's go
vendimia	grape harvest
venga	hurry up, come on
Vía de Cruz	Way of the Cross (Not to be confused with *hacer el viacrucis* – to go on a pub crawl)